D1266746

The Soul of Ann Rutledge

The Soul of
ANN RUTLEDGE

THE TRUE STORY OF
ABRAHAM LINCOLN'S FIRST LOVE

by Bernie Babcock

A BANNER BOOK

EXPOSITION PRESS · NEW YORK

475

*This book is dedicated with love
to its every reader of whatever kind,
class or color, the world around,
in memory of the
Great Emancipator from slavery*

A B R A H A M   L I N C O L N

From the Preface to the First Edition

In the tremendous output of Lincolniana that has been given to literature, it seems strange that no adequate story has been written of one of the greatest loves in history.

Many writers have referred to it and to its moulding power on the lover's after-life. Some have thrown side lights on the character of the woman. Some have mentioned her rare gift of song and her unusual endowment of mind, and one writer has given a careful description of her personal appearance. But so far as careful and exhaustive research shows, all this matter has never been woven into one story.

It is also strange that there has been so much controversy regarding the religious views of Abraham Lincoln, even between those whose faith is based on the evidence required by the Great Teacher when He said, "Ye shall know them by their fruits." Nor should it ever have been taken as an evidence of lack of faith because he did not accept the creedal beliefs of his day, for had not Christ Himself strenuously denied much that was insisted upon in His day, Christianity could never have been possible.

In this story both the love and the faith of one of earth's noblest souls is simply and intimately told.

B. B.

Contents

Introductory Note

Hardly had *The Soul of Ann Rutledge* taken its place among top sellers in times past, when certain honest contributors to the mass of ever growing Lincolniana set out to prove there never was a Lincoln–Rutledge romance. The whole story was a myth, a none-too-clever effort on its author's part to make pure fiction into sturdy fact. This effort, like a fungus growth, has developed to the present proportions which may be judged by the following quotation from a current publication:

> It is difficult to find a Lincoln student who has given any serious attention to the Rutledge story and its ramifications, who is not confident the entire love story as it relates to Lincoln, is only a piece of fiction from untenable sources which can be refuted in its entirety by a chronological record of the people and places associated with the story.

It was so ordained that when the first edition of *The Soul of Ann Rutledge* came out, several persons who had known Lincoln and the Rutledges were yet living. One of these was Henry B. Rankin, who was office boy for Herndon and Lincoln for years and studied law with this firm, and who in after-years wrote several important Lincoln books. Another, and more important person, was the sister of Ann Rutledge, Mrs. Sarah Rutledge Saunders, who, with two sons, was living in California.

Both the sister of Ann Rutledge and Mr. Rankin, after reading *The Soul of Ann Rutledge,* got in touch with its author. Both were pleased with the story. In the young woman who was Ann's teacher in the story, Mr. Rankin recognized his own mother.

Mrs. Saunders, Ann's sister, expressed her great pleasure with the book as one of the happiest surprises of her long life. She wrote to the author as follows:

> Many of the incidents you have mentioned I have heard from my mother. . . . A book so well written upon a subject so closely connected with my father's family, is held, I assure you, with little less than veneration.

This sister of Ann was interviewed for many newspapers, and these interviews generally ended with a question about the love affair of Abe and Ann. Her answer was always a statement that her sister was engaged to marry Abe Lincoln.

Abraham Lincoln's friendship for the Rutledge family was not broken by the passing of Ann, although the Rutledge family and Lincoln left New Salem soon after Ann had gone. During the passing years, Lincoln's interest in Robert Rutledge, Ann's older brother, did not die, and when the dark clouds of the Civil War, which threatened the Union, made the choice of good men important, President Lincoln appointed Robert Rutledge Provost Marshal for the State of Iowa.

It was to Robert Rutledge that William Herndon turned for historical material when he undertook writing his biography of Lincoln. In replies to his enquiries, which covered the entire history of the Rutledge family, Robert Rutledge prepared a 3500-word history for Mr. Herndon. In giving this information Rutledge said, ". . . you make pertinent enquiries concerning my sister and the relations which existed between herself and Mr. Lincoln." Robert Rutledge's reply was climaxed with this statement: "There is no doubt as to the existence of this engagement."

A facsimile copy of this information, which was properly sworn to, was given to the author of *The Soul of Ann Rutledge*, and, together with other family papers and family keepsakes, it is much cherished by the author of the romance of Abe and Ann.

Mothers of book-children, as do mothers of human offspring,

put a value on their legitimacy. The mother of *The Soul of Ann Rutledge* is happy to accept the testimony of Robert Rutledge as the assurance that her best-loved book-child is no myth or ill-born fantasy.

B. B.

The Soul of Ann Rutledge

One April Day

"Ann! Ann! Ann Rutledge! Hallo! Hallo!"

The cheerful voice belonged to a rosy-cheeked girl who shouted in front of Rutledge Inn, one of the straggling group of log houses that made the village of New Salem, Illinois, in 1831.

Pausing in front of the inn, the animated girl repeated her call lustily as she watched for the closed door to open.

"Hallo yourself, Nance Cameron," a clear, musical voice replied from somewhere in the rear of the weather-stained building, and the next moment Ann Rutledge came around the corner.

"Look! Springtime has come! Isn't it splendid to be alive in the springtime? I found them in the thicket!" Pausing she held out an armful of plum branches white with their first bloom.

From the picture of her standing there, an artist might have caught an inspiration. On one side of the background was a vista of open garden and meadow, with a glimpse of forest farther back, and over it all the white-flecked, spring-blue sky.

On the other side was the solid framework that told of days when there had been no meadow or garden, and of the pioneer labor that had wrought the change.

In the foreground of this brown and green and blue setting

stood a slender girl in a pink-sprigged calico dress. Her violet eyes were shaded with dark lashes. Her shapely head was crowned with a wealth of golden hair in which a glint of red seemed hiding. A white kerchief was pinned low about her neck, and across her breast were tied the white strings of a ruffled bonnet which dropped on her shoulders behind. She pressed her face for a moment in the armful of blossoms, sniffing deep, and with the joy of youth exclaimed again, "Isn't it splendid to be alive in the springtime!"

But Nance Cameron had no eye for the artistic at this moment.

"Have you been to the river?"

"River? What's going on at the river?"

"Didn't Davy tell you, nor your father?"

"No, I've just come home across lots from Green's. What's happening at the river?"

"Everything, and everybody's down seeing it happen. Let's go."

"If you'll wait till I fix my flowers."

"Don't wait—drop them or bring them. Everybody but us is there."

Nance Cameron had turned to the roadway. Ann was about to join her when she turned back.

"Bad luck! Bad luck!" shouted Nance. "Don't go back!"

"I forgot to shut the back door."

Nance stopped, made a cross in the dirt and spat on it.

"You don't pay attention to your signs worth a cent," she said, as Ann rejoined her.

"I don't much believe in signs," Ann answered.

"That's where you're silly. A black cat ran across Mrs. Armstrong's path no later than yesterday after she had her soap in the kettle. And wasn't that soap a fizzle? And don't Hannah Armstrong know how to make soap? It was the cat that did it, and if I hadn't changed your luck just now you'd been in for something awful—might never live to marry John McNeil."

Ann laughed, and they started on their way down the road,

that stretched the length of New Salem's one street toward Sangamon River.

"What's going on at the river?" Ann asked again.

"Somebody's ark is stuck on the dam. It got stuck just before dark last night. The crew couldn't get it off and had to wait until morning. They came up to the store to get some drinks. The town men gathered in and you never on this earth heard such roars of laughter as those men let out. Ma couldn't guess what it could be about. When Pa came in he told her there was with the ark crew the funniest tall human being he ever set eyes on. Said his legs reached as high up as a common man's breech belt, his body reached up as high as another man's arms, and his head was up on top of all that. And Pa said he told the funniest stories, and the men nearly died. Pa was laughing yet when he told Ma about it."

"Is the boat stuck yet?"

"She's stuck yet. Dr. Allen and Mentor Graham just went down and I heard them talking. She's on her way to New Orleans with a load of barreled pork and stuff. Davy's been up to the store twice. He says the crew have worked like beavers to get the cargo off the big boat, but that the water is running in bad and the barrels are slipping to the end which sticks out over the dam and she's sure to go over. She's going to make a great splash, and I love splashes. Let's hurry!"

"I hope nobody gets drowned," Ann said.

"Like as not they will, and we'll get to see them fished out. Let's trot a little."

With the inspiring hope of hearing a splash and perhaps seeing the first shocking throes of a drowning, the two girls hastened on down the slope that reached to Rutledge Mill, where the dam was.

It was true, as Nance had said, New Salem was out to witness the unusual sight of a flatboat on the dam where it had been stuck nearly twenty-four hours. It was a river craft of the usual flatboat size, about forty feet long and fifteen wide, and sides six feet high. One end was covered with a roof of boards, and there were other boards fitted with ragged sails to hasten the freight bearer on its long journey of 1800 miles to New Orleans.

The crowd on the river bank and the platform of the mill was lavish with suggestions and advice shouted to the crew working desperately to save the cargo.

Ann Rutledge and Nance Cameron paused a moment to take in the view of the unfortunate boat, whose rear stuck clear of the water and into whose fore the barrels were slowly settling. It seemed nothing could prevent the impending catastrophe.

"Let's get out on the platform. I would like to see that funny tall fellow your father told about," Ann said.

Passing through the mill, deserted for the time by the dusty miller, the girls joined the crowd on the platform and Ann found herself standing by a peculiar appearing personage, a small man of uncertain age, who wore foxed breeches and coon-skin cap, and who had but one good eye which just now was fastened on the fore of the imperiled boat.

"Ole Bar's come back," Ann whispered, punching Nance and turning her eye toward the old man who stood beside her.

Ole Bar was a person of interest, and very peculiar. He was chewing some sort of cud rapidly. When an unusually interesting suggestion was shouted out over the roar of the dam water, he rolled his cud into a hollow made by the loss of two back teeth and kept quiet until the moment of suspense was past, when he made up time working his jaws. Nance only glanced at him now. "I wonder where that tall baboon is?" she said, craning her neck toward the raft.

"See that thar patch of something that ain't no color the Lord God ever made nor no shape He ever seen? Well, that's his hat. He's under it, squattin' in the boat, doin' something to get 'er goin'.'"

"What's he doing?" Ann ventured.

"Eh—that's it," Ole Bar said with a dry smile. "The rest of the crew's runnin' about like chickens with their heads chopped off, and these here galoots along shore is yelping like a pack of coyotes after a buffalo bull. But he's keepin' cool. This kind generally gits something done. Howsomever, that ark's goin' over. I've been numerous in turkey-trottin' and bee-runnin' and bar-killin', but I hain't never before seen an ark in no such fix as this un is."

"Look, Nance," Ann whispered. "He's rising up—look!"

A moment his body partially showed. Then he bent low again. The next moment there was a sudden spurt of water from the bottom of the boat. The water pumping its way out caught the attention of the crowd.

"He's emptying her out!" they cried. "How did he do it?"

The tall figure under the colorless, shapeless hat had now lifted himself, and, as if to straighten his muscles after a long cramped position, he stretched to a height that seemed to be that of a giant, threw out his chest, reached his long arms to a prodigious expanse and took a deep breath.

As he did so Ann felt someone touch her. It was Ole Bar. "Some huggin' he could do with them arms in matin' season—hey, Mollie," he said; and when Ann turned to look at Ole Bar he winked his good eye at her and waited for an answer.

A shout from the crowd made any answer to this remark unnecessary. For a moment the towering youth stood before them like a comical picture, slender, angular, barefooted, his faded yellow breeches scarce more than clearing his knees and showing a pair of spindle legs. His uncolored shirt was flung wide open and over one shoulder was stretched a suspender which held one breeches-leg higher than the other. As the water pumped itself out and the boat began to right, they knew that he had bored a hole.

As the cheers continued, he lifted his shapeless hat and, with the grace of a gentleman, waved it a couple of times at the cheering crowd. Then he pushed back a mop of black hair, clapped his head-covering down on it and turned to help reload the cargo that had been moved into small boats.

To bore a hole in the bottom of a water-filled boat was no great physical task. But the crowd cheered uproariously as the boat righted herself. Men shouted, women waved their bonnets and kerchiefs, and Ann Rutledge shook her branches of wild plums.

Again the ungainly young giant waved his hat.

"He's waving at you, Ann," John McNeil, who had joined the girls, said, coming up behind her. "Wave at him." And she did and laughed as he swung his limp and tattered hat.

"Where do you suppose that kind grow?" Nance asked. "He looks like a giant scarecrow, but he's had lessons in manners the same kind Mentor Graham tells about."

It took but a short time to reload the boat. As she started on her way the cheers died, and most of the crowd went up the hill to the village.

"Let's stay to see the last of it," Ann said to Nance.

"You want him to wave at you some more," John McNeil said to Ann. "Well, go ahead—you'll never see him again."

The boat sailed on. To those on board who looked back a few moments later, the mill and dam were resolving themselves into an indistinct patch of gray and brown, against which a bit of pink, waving something white, stood out. As a farewell answer to the waving of the white, the mellow music of the boat horn came floating back.

The sun went down behind the forests bordering the smoothly flowing Sangamon; the crude craft passed from view.

And yet once again the mellow tones of the primitive horn came floating back over the forest and across the river.

"What a good sound!" Ann exclaimed. "It's soft as the first shadows, and it's strong."

"Yes, strong as that man's arms in mating season—hey, Mollie?" And Nance punched Ann in the side.

The girls laughed merrily. "Isn't Ole Bar funny?" Nance said. "He's just back from an awful exciting trip to Arkansas, or wherever that is. He'll have lots to tell."

"Davy and Father will get his stories. But say, Nance, do sounds make you think of smells?"

"I never thought of such a thing."

"Don't cowbells make you think of hay and dandelions and grass and the smell of the cowlot in the evening?"

"They do go together."

"And don't water running over roots make you think of willow blooms, and don't water dripping over stones sound like ferns when the stems are crushed? And the sound of crows— don't they bring the smell of the field furrows? And don't bees and honey locust, and robins and apple blossoms, go together? I could name a hundred sounds that have smells for partners."

"Yes, but you're funny, Ann, to think of such things."

"Now I have a new pair. The sound of that horn, away off behind the trees, will always make me think of the first plum blossoms. The smell and the sound came together as I shook the branches, and the smell right here seemed to me exactly the same thing told in another way as the sound away over the water. Oh, Nance, don't you love plum blossoms?"

"I don't know whether they're any better than dogwood or haw blooms and I'm not crazy about any of them."

"You're just like John McNeil. John don't like plum blossoms. I nearly cried when he told me he was going to chop out all the plums and wild vines on his place. But those on our place will not be cut. Father has promised me the thicket and the dell on the creek for my flower garden forever."

"I'd rather have a new belt buckle. But let's go."

"I'm ready. I'll race you to the top of the hill before the sun drops behind the trees. One—two—three—off," and with her spring flowers in her arms and her bonnet flying, Ann with Nance ran shouting up the hillside in the slanting rays of the April sun.

CHAPTER 11

In Clary's Grove

The evening of the day the imprisoned flatboat made her way successfully out of New Salem, the Clary Grove gang had a meeting. Windy Batts was expected to return from Springfield, where he had gone to prove his fitness for fellowship with the Clary Grove boys by thrashing a Springfield strong man who had cast aspersions on his character as a pugilist.

Clary Grove was a settlement of a few log houses near New Salem, so called for Bill Clary, the owner of the grove where the select met to swap stories, discuss news and partake of real liquor.

Every newcomer to the vicinity was sized up. If Clary Grove was friendly, so much the better for the newcomer. He might not become a member of the gang, though. Indeed few were allowed to sit in close fellowship about the fire with the gang, but he would at least be let alone.

Windy Batts had expressed a desire to be of the gang. He was, however, looked upon with a degree of suspicion, as he had done some exhorting for the Hard Shells, and Clary Grove looked askance at religion in any form, and while he had boasted of "dingblasting the daylights out of them shoutin' Methodists,"

Clary Grove was not satisfied that he was proper stuff to fellowship with them and their whiskey.

They awaited his return from Springfield, where he was to prove his pugilistic ability, with some interest.

The cool, spring air, with the tang of frost not yet safely out of it, made a fire comfortable, and a bright blaze burned between the two smooth logs on which the gang roosted.

Buck Thompson, the luckiest horse trader in that section, and Ole Bar were the first to arrive. Ole Bar sat beside the fire, his jaws working industriously and his one good eye shining like a spark. No one of the gang had ever been able to learn what misfortune had befallen the lost eye of Ole Bar.

That he had been "cleaned of it right and proper" all agreed. Opinion was divided, however, as to the cause or method, one portion believing a bear had clawed it out, because of his familiarity with bears, and others holding to the opinion that some specimen of womankind was responsible for the loss, because of his oft-expressed unfriendly feeling toward women.

Jo Kelsy, a fat and favorite brother of the clan, who was always ready with a new story about a ghost or a witch from his one treasure, an inherited copy of Shakespeare, was the third to arrive.

His usual costume was varied slightly. He came hobbling in, one foot encased in a moccasin. Ole Bar glanced at his mismated feet.

"What's bit ye, Jo?" he asked.

"My wife, she dropped a five-gallon crock on my foot," he answered.

"Good thing it wasn't your head, for be it known by man and bars, them as mixes up with wimmen has heads softer than their feet."

Jo laughed good naturedly. Then the three talked of the raft and the ungainly youth who had resorted to the homely but efficient expedient of boring a hole.

"I've seen some legs in my day," Jo Kelsy observed, "but none long as his'n."

"Ain't no longer than yours is, Dumplin'," said Ole Bar. "Yours reaches to the ground and his'n don't go no further. According to my way of figgerin' his legs wasn't so numerous when it comes to length as his head. That galoot's got a long head."

A couple more of the gang dropped in, and the talk continued about the raft and the head raftsman. "Ever see anything like it? Wouldn't think a backwoodsman could tell such stories as he did last night, would ye?"

"Nor know enough to get an ark floating when she was stuck so tight that God hisself couldn't stick her no tighter."

"McNeil was figgerin' on her cargo to see what it was worth."

"Trust McNeil for figgerin' the worth of a cargo—or anything else."

"Ann Rutledge—eh?"

They laughed. Then one said, "I heard him tellin' Hill him and Ann was goin' to marry and have a big infare. But her Pappy won't let her till next year. She has to git more schoolin'."

"He better git while gittin's good. James Rutledge is fixed, and he sets more store by Ann than the whole other eight of 'em."

"McNeil knows all that. But here comes Kit Parsons. Wonder what's kept him late? Kit, you're late."

"Yeh," and he sat down by the fire.

"What's extry? Been stealin' anything or gettin' religion?"

"Same thing as gettin' religion," he said. "Been fulfillin' the Scripture injunction."

"Which one?"

"Been replenishin' and multiplyin'."

"Mollie got another litter?" Ole Bar asked with a show of interest.

"Just one this year. But I calculate that a man what grubs for three which arrives in two years is somewhat religious."

"Bars is that religious," the one-eyed man observed, "only when they pursue the course of nature they don't blame it on religion."

After a laugh Ole Bar said solemnly to Kit, "If you young fellers knew what was good fer you you'd let wimmin alone,"

"Where'd you learn so much about wimmin?" Jo asked.

"From bars. Bars rubs noses at matin' time and tears the ears offen each other when the cubs has to be fed. Let wimmin alone and save the wear on your noses and ears."

"How's a body going to leave any ancestry if he don't never git no place near a woman?" Buck Thompson asked.

"Ancestry?" repeated Ole Bar. "Well, what under heaven is these little, wet-nosed ancestry good fer anyhow? Never had no ancestry myself and I'm gettin' along all right—got along all right while I was in Arkansas, and anybody that can do that don't need to worry about leavin' no ancestry."

"Tell us about Arkansas," was the next demand.

Ole Bar shifted his cud into its receptacle and said, "Well, as you all know, in bar hunts I've been numerous, but I hain't never seen no such bars as grow in Arkansas. The bars in Arkansas is the most promiscuous I've ever seen and don't give a damn for nobody. But, Squire, let's licker up. I'm gettin' so dry I'm takin' the rattles," and he reached for the bottle which was passed around.

"Bars in Arkansas grows so fat they can't wobble. You fellers here that think you're gettin' the real thing when you bag the chipper growlers and shite pokers of these parts don't know nothin' about what's growing in Arkansas. Them bars rear up into the heavens high as that feller that plugged the ark."

"That smells rather tall," Buck Thompson observed, but Ole Bar paid no attention.

"The woods in Arkansas is ankle deep with acorns and berries and other bar food. Everybody there eats bar, bar ham and bar sassage. The beds is covered with bar skins. They don't use small skins like wild cat fer nothin' 'cept piller covers."

"Do they have hoss tradin' in them parts?" Buck Thompson inquired.

"Hoss tradin'? Well, I should say yeh. You galoots think you swap hosses, but in Arkansas——"

"Hallo, fellers," shouted someone in the outer circle of light.

"It's Windy Batts," several declared at once, and immediately the man whose qualifications to become a member of the charmed group had been put to the test, entered the circle of light.

He was scrutinized and with not an altogether approving eye. His arm was done up in a sling. The forefinger of his right hand was wrapped in a red calico handkerchief. Something like a knob stuck out back of one ear which was covered with a square of muslin, giving it the appearance of a pat of butter. One eye was black, and both legs seemed to be stiff. Greetings were brief. The main question was, "Who whipped?"

"Yeh—who hollered?" was asked.

Windy drew near the fire. "It was a great fight," he began. "The greatest fight that was ever fought in Springfield. We rolled over and over, him sometimes on top and me sometimes under. It was a fearful fight. Court turned out to see it and an Indian chief was there. He said he never seen nothing like it."

"Who whipped?" was again asked.

"Yeh—who hollered?"

Ignoring these questions, Windy continued, "The big Indian and the judge of the court both said they hadn't never seen such sledge-hammer blows as I hit. It was them blows that put my shoulder out of joint. But I fixed his eye. You couldn't have told it from a knothole in a burnt tree. Time he aimed a second sock-dolager at me I was ready. The crowd roared like a camp meeting. We fell to it. He got a straddle of my head and chawed my finger. There wasn't no place for me to git hold, owing to the fact my head was pinned in twix his legs. Jean britches didn't taste well and was ungodly tough. But I was resolute. I found the right place and I chawed like hell. But would he let go of my finger? No, and I finally had to knock half his teeth out to git my finger out his mouth."

"You tanned him—hey?"

"You mauled him, Windy?"

"You beat the Springfield stuffing out of him?"

"And nobody parted you?"

Ignoring these questions, Windy took a fresh start. "And there's no telling how long it might have lasted, us two going round and round and up and down and every which way. I was eternally mauling the ding-blasted daylights out of him when the judge got hold of me and asked as a favor if I wouldn't put off the finish till next day. He said he couldn't get nobody into court if I didn't and so I—I hollered."

There was a moment of profound silence. Windy shifted his weight from one stiff leg to the other, stroked his bandaged arm and sighed.

"Spit in his ashes!"

It was the voice of Jack Armstrong that broke the painful stillness. Immediately every man emptied the contents of his mouth, with no small force, into the fire, which voiced its protest by a vigorous spitting and sputtering.

Then Windy was given some advice.

"This ain't no place fer you. You go join them Hard Shells that's fixin' fer a ten days' fightin' match with the devil. They have the same runnin' off at the mouth as you have, but they hain't never drawed no devil's blood yet, and that's your crowd."

Windy's lips moved as if to speak.

"Roll in your molasses sucker and trampoose," was the order.

"Yeh—trampoose," was the repeated order. "Go fight the devil."

"The devil—that's the Clary Grove gang," he muttered as he turned away.

"Devil-fighter," some one said as his limping figure disappeared in the darkness.

"If the devil pays any more heed to him than he would to a skit fly he's a blame bigger ass than I've ever took him to be," Ole Bar observed. "Let's licker up."

CHAPTER III

The Rail Splitter

It was two months after the flatboat stuck on the dam at New Salem and the day following a quiet election in the village, that Nance Cameron ran over to Rutledge Inn with news of great importance for Ann.

"Long Shanks has arrived," she announced without ceremony.

"Long Shanks?" Ann questioned. "Who is Long Shanks?"

"The giant scarecrow, the big baboon," Nance answered.

"Baboon," Ann repeated. "Nance, what are you talking about?"

"My land, Ann Rutledge, have you forgotten the unhinged giant you waved plum blossoms at—the captain of the flatboat who looked like sin but knew how to use his hat like a gentleman?"

"Oh!" answered Ann. "Has *he* come?"

"Yes. He got here yesterday. They didn't have anybody to help at election. Mentor Graham asked him if he could write. He said he could make his rabbit's foot, and so he helped. Mr. Graham says he can write well. Besides, he told them stories, and they liked that. Last night he came to our house."

"Tell me about him. What does he look like close to?"

"He's the homeliest man God ever put breath into. His legs

run down into feet so long he can't find anything big enough to stick them under, and his arms are nearly as long as his legs. He has a big head, big nose, big mouth, big ears, lots of black hair, and he's hard and horny and knotty like a tree—and as green, too."

"Did he talk to you?"

"No, he didn't pay me any heed at all, but he and Ma got to be good friends before he'd been in the house an hour. She was tired half to death putting up berries and trying to get supper. She put Johnnie watching the baby and he let him roll down the steps. The new man heard him crying and went right out and got him. In five minutes the baby was laughing. This made Ma feel better and she got talking, and first thing I knew he was helping her wash dishes and telling her about what he saw in New Orleans and down the Mississippi. He talks better than he looks."

"How does he talk? Has he a big, deep voice and mellow, like the sound of the horn over the tree and river?"

"No, indeed. He sets out thin sounding, but his voice seems to work down into his chest as he talks and he sounds pretty good. After supper Pa brought in the cider. Mr. Graham came over and Dr. Allen, and they got Long Shanks talking and didn't want him to quit. Mentor Graham took a great liking to him. He lived in Kentucky once and then in Indiana. He asked about the folks in these parts and when he heard Jo Kelsy owns a Shakespeare he said he was going to try to borrow it, said he's read the Bible till he knew it by heart and the Constitution and some other things but never seen a Shakespeare. When Mr. Graham told him he had fifty books, his dull gray eyes turned bright as new candles. He's terrible interested in books, but he don't have any time for girls."

"How do you know?"

"'Cause. Ma asked him if he saw the girl waving at him, when the boat stuck. He said, 'Yes'm—wasn't it kind of her?'

"Ma said, 'She's the prettiest girl in town.'

"He said, 'Yes'm—isn't that nice?'

"Ma said, 'She's the smartest girl in town.'

"He said, 'Yes'm—it's worth while to be smart!'

"Ma told him you was going to marry John McNeil. He said, 'They all do it.' And he never even asked your name.

"I tell you what; you drop past tomorrow afternoon before supper. He'll be there then. He won't look at you, he's so funny. But you can see him."

It was with as much interest as a person goes to a show that Ann Rutledge went to the Cameron home the next afternoon. She was doomed to disappointment.

"He's gone," Nance informed her.

"Where?"

"Gone out to split rails for some folks that have come in from Indiana and are taking a homestead near Turtle Ford. He's going to split enough rails to fence the clearing. He's to get one yard of brown jeans dyed with white walnut bark for every four hundred rails. It's to make some new breeches."

"That's an awful lot of work for a pair of pants."

"Yes, but look at the length of his legs. A fellow with legs like that will always have to work extra to keep them covered."

"I wanted to see him."

"He's coming back. I heard him telling Pa he was going to open a store here for a man named Offutt. His wares haven't come yet. They will be here by the time the new breeches are ready. Then you can see him. You'll think him half-baboon and half-giraffe and he won't even notice you, only to say 'Yes'm' and pull off his hat."

"Does he have any name? You didn't tell it."

"Name? Oh, yes." And Nance laughed. "He's named after Abraham, of the Abraham, Isaac and Jacob family. The rest of his name is Lincoln."

"Abraham Lincoln," Ann repeated. "I don't think that's such a bad-sounding name."

John McNeil called at the Rutledge home the night young Lincoln went to Turtle Ford to earn his new pants. After the family had gone to bed and Ann was left to say good night to the young man she was engaged to, he said, "Ann, I thought that fellow was captain of the boat and maybe owned some of the cargo. He's nothing but a rail splitter."

"He didn't use his hat like a rail splitter."

"He's picked up a few lessons in manners somewhere—maybe saw somebody doing it in New Orleans."

"No—because it was on his way down that he lifted his hat."

"Well, I don't know where he got it, but he's only a rail splitter just the same. Hasn't a cent in the world. Didn't know it was a rail splitter waving to you, did you?"

"It wasn't me he waved at. He never heard of me and don't know yet that I am living. It was the flowers he liked and I'm glad he likes flowers if he is a rail splitter."

"I'd like to know, Ann, why you take on so over flowers. What are they good for?"

"Good for? What a funny question. What is the song of birds good for and the fragrance of flowers and the beauty of ferns? What is the music of running brooks good for and the splendor of gold and red sunsets—what are any of them good for?"

"That's just what I'm asking," John McNeil said seriously. "What *are* they good for? Can't eat them, can you? Can't wear them, can you? Can't sell them, can you? or trade them or swap them for anything? Women are such funny folks and don't know a thing about values. But I'm going to leave the plum thicket another year and the corner in the pasture where the blue flowers grow you like to pick."

"Thank you, John—thank you a whole lot"; and happy because of his promise, Ann kissed John McNeil good night.

CHAPTER IV

The Pilgrim

A few days after Abraham Lincoln had entered service to split rails for a new pair of breeches, he came to town late one afternoon to get an ax.

After tarrying a short time to tell a story or two, he started back about sundown, his ax, on the handle of which was swung a bundle, over his shoulder.

As twilight gathered, the ungainly youth took his way along the road that ran not far from the smoothly flowing Sangamon. His strides were long and easy, and, away from the small habitations and contrivances of mankind, he seemed to become one with the big things of nature, and what was sometimes considered lack of grace seemed now an easy expression of reserve force.

The roar of the mill dam sounded musical as if the twilight were softening its daytime boisterous tumult.

The falling dew seemed loosening up the fragrance of the woods, the subtle breath of tangled vines and trailing roses, with sometimes a more decided fragrance, as when the full-sized foot of the pedestrian brushed into a bed of wild mint.

As he rounded the skirt of the bluff, the rosy-tinted sky seemed suddenly to withdraw itself, and the timbers upon the summit to move themselves slowly against the crimson and fading gold, like a row of shadowy sentinels gathered for the night.

A tinkling gurgle from an irregular, dark spot against the foot of the bluff told of a ravine and the running stream, whose musical babble, as it made its way to the river, sounded like the prattle of a child compared to the river's volume falling by the mill.

As he took his way in the gathering gray of night, the long-limbed youth cast giant shadows, subtle, indistinct shadows far across the road and into other shadows, where they merged into the formless gloom and were lost.

While yet rounding the bluff, he heard the barking of a dog and then the tinkle of a cowbell. Common sounds these were, but coming on the stillness from the heights above they lent a sort of musical enchantment to the quiet and enfolding mystery of night. Then a human voice was heard, a woman's voice that seemed to burst suddenly into the flower of a full-blown song.

The youth slowed up a bit and listened. The words thrown out by the ringing voice sounded clearly:

> "I'm a pilgrim
> And I'm a stranger;
> I can tarry, I can tarry but a night."

The young man stopped. The song was unusual to him. The clear voice took the notes unhesitatingly and rolled them in melodious movement as she sang the words "pi-i-i-ilgrim" and "stra-a-a-anger," and then hurrying on gladly, as if it were a matter for great rejoicing that she could tarry but a night.

The youth dropped his ax and bundle to the ground and turned his face toward the bluff casting its long shadows. The bell tinkled a moment in the gathering gloom. Then the voice rang out again on the evening hush:

> "Do not detain me,
> For I am going
> To where the streamlets are ever flowing."

Again there was the peculiar rolling fall and rise on the syllables. Again the gladness of some exultation, then the refrain "I'm a pilgrim" with its confidence and its melody.

The voice was nearer now. There was no sound or sight of any moving object on the bluff, but she was there somewhere and seemed coming nearer.

The tinkle of the cowbell made an interlude. Then again the voice of singing, whether nearer or farther now, he did not question. He was listening to the words:

> "Of that country
> To which I'm going
> My Redeemer, my Redeemer is the light.
> There is no sorrow
> Nor any sighing
> Nor any sin there, nor any dying."

The mysterious singer on the heights was farther away now. The voice was growing fainter as the refrain rang into the stillness, "I'm a pilgrim—and I'm a stranger—I can tarry—I can tarry——"

The youth leaned forward and listened, breathlessly. But the voice was dying and the tinkle of the bell came on the stillness, faint as a memory.

After standing a moment, the listener in the shadows made ready to go on. When he turned to pick up his ax and bundle, he found his hat in his hands. When he had removed it he did not remember. Mechanically he placed it on his head and started on his way.

The red and purple of the earlier evening showing through the trunks of the trees crowning the bluff was giving way now to the silvery green of the rising moon.

With his ax over his shoulder the figure paused a moment for a last look upward and then moved on.

But he did not feel the same. He had undergone some change. What was it? Within his breast the song had raised something intensely alive—something like hunger, fierce yet very tender; something like strange pain; something like wild joy; something like unsatisfied longing, together with unmeasured satisfaction. What was it? He did not know. Mysterious to him as was the singer, was now the effect of the singing.

Yet out of the mingled sensation of unrest and satisfaction, suddenly stirred into life, there came to the youth thoughts of his mother.

His mother had been a pilgrim on a journey. He had heard her say so many times. But the burden of her song had been "Earth is a desert drear." He had heard her sometimes try to sing. But she did not go shouting. She suffered on the way, endured, was patient, and at the last she reached a groping hand for something strong to hold her back from that country to which she believed she was going. It was with a twitching of his muscles and a quiver of the big strong mouth that he thought of the passing on of his mother.

But here was a pilgrim happy, shouting, even jubilant. Who was she? What manner of person could she be? His curiosity was aroused.

As he strode on toward Turtle Ford the falling waters of the dam softened their roar into an indistinct murmur, and then, like the voice of the singer and the tinkle of the bell, blended into the quiet, broken only by the call of a whippoorwill or the whirr of a bat's wing.

The moon rose above the lacey darkness of the timber line. The rail splitter had had no supper. Once he stopped and gathered some berries. But he was not thinking of food. The eternal mystery of the awakening of one's other self had both breathed through and enfolded him. He was not hungry. He tossed the berries down by the roadside. His pace quickened as he neared the clearing. He did not understand, but for some reason he himself experienced a lifted-up sensation. It was as if the conquering confidence and joy of the unknown singer had been contagious.

At the edge of the clearing he stopped. The shack and pigpen and few rail fences stood out in the moonlight like the skeleton

of something to be clothed with a body. The dogs came out and
barked, but crept back satisfied at sight of the tall figure. He
stepped up to the door of the shack. The snoring of a man told
him his approach had not disturbed the sleeping family.

He turned toward the end of the cabin where a ladder stood
which he mounted. At the square opening which served as door
and window to the loft, he paused and looked in, and by the
moon's indistinct light he saw the three boys of the family lying
on a pallet. The dull hum of mosquitoes sounded.

He turned back to the ladder, and on its top, with his back
resting against the cabin, he sat and looked out into the night.
In the light all was beautiful; even the piles of brush were
softened until they looked like the gray and silver tendrils of
giant vines piled by titanic fairies, and the trunks of trees were
columns in some mysterious and endless cathedral canopied
with silvered green.

Across the wilds of the forest, which in the magic of the
night and the moon were so beautiful, the thoughts of the youth
again traveled back to his childhood and its mysteries, and he
seemed to see again a very small grave in a lonesome spot beside
which his mother cried and declared with tears and choking
voice that she could not go away and leave it forever. To the boy
who looked on, this had seemed strange. Why should she weep
because she could not take a grave from Kentucky to Indiana,
the new home—and such a tiny little grave? It had been a mystery. Later he came to answer the mystery of it by calling it
"mother love." He thought of that grave, far away in Kentucky,
as he sat on the ladder. Then he thought of the grave of the
mother who had wept beside the little grave—two graves.

Some time he too would fill a grave somewhere—and so would
the singer on the heights. What was life after all? Its end was
the same for all—whether a tiny grave or one long enough even
for him? The question seemed to mock itself and laugh.

Then the voice of the singer rang clear again—a pilgrim rejoicing, shouting—such a glad pilgrim, and again he felt himself

impelled to the heights from which it had come—felt himself a creature of some fresh-born force he could no more fathom than explain.

A wild cat screamed down the creek. The three boys thumped the floor, seeking in their sleep to destroy the mosquitoes. The dogs scratched under the house. The man snored. Once the baby cried and the mother soothed it.

These voices and sounds seemed a part of the secrets of the night and of the strange awakening that possessed him with the pleasure and pain of its mystery.

There was a sound, however, that came with the first pink of the morning that seemed in some unknown way to hold the key to the mystery of his strangely aroused hunger—a hunger born whether for good or ill he knew not.

With the first stirring of life at the new day, a song bird just at the edge of the clearing sent out its call, clear as the voice of the singer on the bluff and, in the imagination of the inquiring youth, like it, glad and unafraid.

But the bird was calling for a mate—one of its own kind— one which would answer its call.

Again the call rang out penetrating and joyful.

The young man listened. Then a smile of satisfaction lit his homely face, for from somewhere down in the tangle of the creek banks, one of its own kind was answering the call.

The hidden singer in the clearing called again, even throwing more life and gladness into the song. Again the answer came from the unseen one of like kind, a little closer now. They were moving toward each other. The silent listener had not made a study of birds. Yet now he was quite sure that somewhere they would meet in the wide expanse of overlaced branches and would mate.

Again his mind went back to the singer of the bluff—and her challenging call. Who or what manner of woman was she? He wondered.

When the man who had been snoring awoke with the first

streaks of day, the ringing of an ax sounded on his ear. "If he don't beat anything to bite them trees down and eat them up, I'm a liar. He must have been at it all night."

"He needs breeches—needs them powerful bad," his wife replied.

"Must want to go a courtin'," was his comment.

"Courtin' or no courtin', he'll be ketched by the sheriff if he don't git some new breeches right soon. His is fixin' to leave him. I'm skeered every time he jumps over the fence."

CHAPTER V

Swapping Hosses

Not more than a fortnight after Windy Batts had been weighed in the balance by the Clary Grove boys, Mrs. Mirandy Benson ran over to Rutledge's to discuss a few news items.

Mrs. Benson was Phoebe Jane Benson's mother. Phoebe Jane Benson had never been kissed by a human man—her mother the authority for the statement. "No start, no finish," was Mrs. Benson's oft-quoted statement as touching the delicate question of the preservation of female virtue. "For this reason, Mis' Rutledge, I'm dead set against huggin'. There's never no tellin' where huggin' will end, and Phoebe Jane shan't get no opportunity."

But it was not of hugging that she now talked. "Mis' Rutledge," she said, "Windy Batts has been dipped and is going to set out preachin' for the Hard Shells and will hold a meetin' near New Salem. It's set to his credit, I say, that he chose to unite with the Hard Shells instead of the Clary Grove gang. Since Windy Batts has been keepin' company with Phoebe Jane, I've been uncommon interested. He has a powerful flow of language, and will make a famous exhorter."

A second topic of conversation was the tall clerk who was in charge of the new store opened by Offutt. "He's the one that helped Mentor Graham election day and has been chopping rails since on Turtle Ford.

"Everybody in town's been in the store, and the men hang around every evenin'. Phoebe Jane, she's been, too. He's an awful friendly fellow, scraped up a speakin' with Phoebe Jane and asked her who in these parts could sing. She told him she could sing, bass or tenor, either he liked. Phoebe Jane was quite took up with him and wanted to ask him to meetin'. But he's too friendly. These friendly young fellows must be watched. He might be all right. Then again he mightn't, and if he should take a huggin' spell like some young fellows takes, with them arms no tellin' what might happen. I told Phoebe Jane not to let out too much rope, especially since Windy Batts got religion."

It was true the new clerk at Offutt's store had inquired who about New Salem could sing. Having been unable to learn anything satisfactory from the girl he had asked, he put the question to several men who chanced to be in the store. The only result of his questioning was to bring out a story about a girl in New Salem who had a "singin'" in her head for which a plaster of "psalm tunes," applied to the feet to draw the singing down, had been prescribed. Unsatisfied, young Lincoln determined to keep his ears open and try to discover for himself.

Meantime there were many to get acquainted with, and when Bill Clary himself invited the new man to the Grove, he at once accepted the invitation.

Ole Bar, Buck Thompson, Jo Kelsy and several others had gathered early and were discussing the guest that was to arrive shortly. Buck Thompson was especially interested. He was in possession of a horse with a head three times too large and legs four times too small for his bony body. Some fatal defect in the horse made him, as Buck Thompson confidently told the crowd, "not worth a chaw," and this horse he was going to try to swap Lincoln, "sights unseen."

Speculation had just started as to the outcome of Buck's horse trade when Clary and the tall stranger arrived.

"His name is Abe Lincoln," Clary advised,

"'Linkhorn' is what they called me over in Indiana."

"Paws, Abry Linkhorn," Ole Bar said, extending his hand and casting his one good eye with approval on the stranger.

The few brief formalities having been dispensed with, the group settled down to stories and discussions, Ole Bar leading off with a graphic description of many of the wonders of Arkansas, and its riches of soil and abundance of game. "There was one feller down thar had a sow," he declared gravely. "She stole an ear of corn and took it down whar she slept at night. She spilt a grain or two on the ground, and then she lay on them. And, gentlemen, believe it or not, before morning the corn shot up, pushed on right through her and the percussion killed her. Next morning she was found flat as a pancake and three-inch corn sticking like green har through her spotted hide."

"I swear!" exclaimed Jo Kelsy.

"Don't cuss; jes go down to that country and see," was Ole Bar's comment.

When Abe Lincoln's time came he was asked for the lizard story he had told at the store the night the flatboat stuck on the dam. In an inimitable way he told the story, joining heartily with the others in the boisterous laughter it called forth, but neither this nor any other of the stories told diverted the mind of Buck Thompson from the main question, this being, "Is he as green as he looks? Will he swap hosses?"

"Don't happen to have a hoss you want to trade, do ye?" Buck at last indifferently questioned.

The interest of the company was at once centered on the answer.

"Want to swap hosses?" Abe Lincoln asked good naturedly.

"Well, I dunno. Do you happen to own a hoss of any kind?"

"Yep," answered the visitor. "Such as it is, I own a hoss."

An expression of pleasure showed on the face of Buck Thompson.

"What sort is he?" Buck asked.

"Who said it was a 'he'?"

The crowd laughed.

"What kind is she?" Buck corrected.

"Well," answered the youth as if weighing the matter, "she ain't nothing extra on looks, but she can stand up under as much hard work as any hoss in these parts."

"How old is she?"

"I dunno to a day—not very old."

"Stand without hitchin'?"

"Never's been hitched to anything in her life."

"Saddle hoss, I take it. Ain't any mustang, is it?"

"Not a drop of mustang in the critter, I swear it."

"Ain't blind in one eye, is she?"

"No."

"How's her legs?"

"Can't lie, partner. She's stiff in the legs."

"Stiff in the legs, eh? How about her teeth?"

"Haven't counted them."

"Ever had the botts?"

"Not as I know of."

"Or winded?"

"Not since I've had her."

"Want to swap hosses?" Buck asked.

"What you got?" Abe Lincoln asked with interest.

"I got one what'll stand hitched. I'm goin' to be honest as you and tell you my hoss has stiff legs. From what I git, my hoss is just about such a hoss as your hoss. How'll you swap, sight unseen?"

Abe Lincoln asked a few questions which proved to Buck Thompson beyond a doubt that the lanky youth was as green as he looked on the horse-trading proposition, and he was delighted both for the stakes involved and the effect of his deal on the Clary Grove boys, when Abe Lincoln agreed to the trade.

"Where's your hoss at?" Buck inquired.

"Out back of Offutt's store. Where's yourn?"

"He's to home—but I'll bring him."

"Any rush?" Lincoln inquired. "Morning's not far off."

But Buck had no notion of taking chances on letting the horse trader consider over night. He insisted on winding up the trade in the bright light of the moon in front of Offutt's store. The crowd agreed to be present, and immediately afterward, with singing and loud talking, the Clary Grove gang took their way to New Salem to Offutt's store. Buck Thompson went after his horse, and Abe Lincoln disappeared in the shadows of the store to find his.

Buck was the first to arrive. Not even the moonlight could cast any redeeming qualities on the beast that hobbled after him. The crowd looked it over and laughed uproariously. Buck grinned with satisfaction at the sight-unseen trade he was about to make and questioned half fearfully if the greenhorn would stand by his agreement.

The appearance in the distance of a tall and shadowy figure approaching with long, easy strides was not reassuring. Certainly he was neither leading nor driving a horse. The company looked. As he came nearer they saw he carried something. Its shadow blended with that of his body.

"He's got his hoss under his arm or on his back," one observed.

Buck was looking anxiously.

"Bet two to one it's a goat," Jo Kelsy said.

This sounded good to Buck. "Goat!" he said with evident pleasure. Then they looked again. The next minute he cleared the last lap of shadow and came into the light in the open space.

There was a moment of impressive silence.

"My hoss is this kind—one of the most useful animals in this neck of the woods," and he placed a sawhorse before them.

There was a moment of impressive silence, then the angry voice of Buck Thompson.

"You're a liar," he cried, greatly angered by the roar of laughter that had greeted the speech.

A dead hush fell on the company. A fight seemed the next excitement. Every eye was on Lincoln.

"Don't get riled up," he said good-naturedly, "especially after I told you I was tellin' the truth. Didn't I tell you her legs was stiff?"

"Yeh," roared Buck, "and you told me she had two good eyes—eh, boys?" and he turned to the crowd standing close about.

"Easy now," Abe Lincoln remonstrated. "I didn't say she had two good eyes. You asked if she was blind in one eye, and I said, 'No, she ain't blind in no eye.'"

"You said she had all her teeth," Buck challenged.

"Naw, what I said was, 'She hasn't never lost no teeth, far as I know.' Can you see any place where they have come out?"

Clearly the new clerk had the best of the trade. Buck Thompson stood to his bargain. The horse was passed to Lincoln. He looked it over. Something in the ungainly figure and the big-headed horse brought a smile. Yet they waited. What would he do next—or say?

"Partner," he said to Buck after the examination, "I wouldn't know what use to make of this here critter. I can't make no sight-unseen proposition, but I'd give you two bits for my own hoss back."

CHAPTER VI

"Fixin' fer the Angels"

Offutt's new store under the management of Abe Lincoln came
to be, almost immediately, the chief point of interest in the
village.

Business was never so rushing that the genial long-legged
newcomer could not find time for a friendly greeting or a new
story.

Jo Kelsy, famed as the best Shakespeare scholar New Salem
boasted, soon discovered a kindred spirit in Abe Lincoln, and
was delighted to find in him a pupil so hungry to get acquainted
with Bill Shakespeare.

Mentor Graham, the Scotch schoolmaster, dropped into the
store because he soon discovered that, although the youth who
had assisted him on election day had had no opportunity of going
to school, he was far more advanced in general knowledge than
any pupil in his school, and the fact pleased him that Abe
Lincoln wanted to study grammar with him, and after a while
higher branches.

Even Dr. Allen, the busiest and most conscientious Predestinarian in Sangamon County, cultivated the acquaintance of

the Lincoln youth, and he soon discovered that the uncommon young fellow, who seemed to be everybody's friend, was not given to social drink, and this pleased Dr. Allen, who boldly preached that liquor was poison and stood for its total abstinence.

The Clary Grove boys visited the store, and when several of them happened to be in at the same time, the laughter and boisterous talk could be heard the length of New Salem.

Ann Rutledge had not yet been at the new store. She had heard from it, however, through her brother Davy, two years younger than herself, and her half-grown sister, known as "Sis Rutledge," both having formed the acquaintance of Abe Lincoln and both having immediately become his staunch admirers.

Ole Bar was in the store one afternoon when Davy came in.

"Davy," Abe Lincoln said, "see here"; and putting three long fingers gently into his pocket he drew out a handful of tiny rabbits. "Their mother got killed. I put the poor little things in my pocket. Know anybody that will take care of them?"

Ole Bar opened his good eye and listened.

"Sure. Ann, she'll do it. Ann Rutledge takes care of blind cats, lame dogs, lousy calves, birds with broken wings, and all such things."

Abe Lincoln had placed the rabbits carefully in his hat and handed it to Davy.

"Want them back?" the boy questioned as he turned toward the door.

"No—but hurry back with my hat. I'm goin' out with Kelsy while he fishes, and read about a Jew who wanted a pound of flesh."

The expression on Ole Bar's small eye was one of concentrated disgust.

"Men's not what they used to be," he observed, chewing violently.

"I reckon not," Abe Lincoln observed.

"These times they wear whiskers on their upper lip, and breeches buttoned up the fore, but I don't see as it's give them any more wits."

Abe Lincoln did not answer this, but asked a question. "Who sings about these diggin's? It's some woman who has a way of her own."

"All wimmin sings; wimmin birds sings, and wimmin bull-frogs sings, and human wimmin sings. But whether they be scaled or feathered or diked out in calico and combs, their singin' is to git the men of their kind. Take the advice of Ole Bar, my long-legged son, Abry Linkhorn, and let all wimminkind alone. Furthermore, don't try to start no love-makin' with Ann Rut-ledge and blame it onto rabbits. I've heard said Ann Rutledge can outsing a bird. If she can, it's for John McNeil. John McNeil, he's worth ten thousand dollars—so they say. Hain't this worth singin' for?"

"The one I'm talking about wasn't singin' for any man's money."

"How do you know?"

"It wasn't that kind of a song."

Ole Bar laughed. "Sonny," he said, "you're as green as you look. But why don't you go up to the meetin' what Windy Batts's started? All the singers will be there. Windy's trying to scare the devil out of his own den by his fierce preachin'. Last night he called the whole Clary Grove tribe by name and told them the devil was goin' to pepper them with burnin' fiery sulphur in chunks as big as Rutledge Mill forever and aye unless they crawled up on the rock of ages. They'll be going to meetin' their-selves right soon, and if he don't know any better sense than readin' cusses at them out of the Holy Scriptures and pointin' the finger of scorn at them before the people, they'll learn him some."

It was this same evening Abe Lincoln decided to go to Clary Grove in search of Kelsy, from whom he wanted to borrow the Shakespeare. The Grove boys were in council. An indignation meeting was being held. Kit Parsons had just been quoting Windy Batts, who had the night before consigned those Clary Grove sinners, root and branch, to burn forever, and it had been just about decided that he, and the horse he had purchased to start on an itinerary after his New Salem meeting, should be treated to a coat of tar and feathers.

"That deer-faced hypocrite tells how God sent his angels to git Daniel out of the lion's den, how he sent angels to git them three fool Jews out of the fiery furnace. He says them kind of angels guard the Hard Shells, saves them from their enemies and gits them out of tight places. We're needin' some angels in this section. Let's coax them down. Let's anoint this belly-aching coward with hot tar and feathers—both him and his horse, till we make him look like the buzzard he is. Then we'll set by and see how long it takes them angels to git the feathers picked off."

A laugh had followed this speech. It was about this time that Abe Lincoln appeared.

"Howdy!" he said in his most friendly manner.

They returned his greeting, but it was evident he was not wanted. They asked him, however, for a suggestion as to how best to punish "a moon-eyed pole cat that hain't nothin' better to do than stir up a stink about hell fire and brimstone, and call out the names of them picked by the devil to supply the roasts."

"I wouldn't take it to heart about his fiery talk. He can't hurt God with his spittin' and sputterin', and so long as God's all right, the rest of us needn't worry," Lincoln said, before answering the request asked. "As to punishin' a 'moon-faced pole cat,' I'd plug him up in some tight corner, poke sin out of him—and he'd punish hisself, gentlemen—punish hisself."

Abe Lincoln got the book and went away. After he had gone, the Clary boys put their heads together, and before they had separated for the night, the tar-and-feathers plan had been temporarily abandoned.

CHAPTER VII

"Sick 'Em, Kitty"

The afternoon following his rather unwelcome visit to Clary Grove, Abe Lincoln was invited by Kit Parsons to attend religious services that night. From the manner of the invitation the storekeeper gathered that there might be something interesting on foot, and he decided to go.

Some changes had been made in the meeting place since the gathering of the year before. At that time Satan had moved the dogs, so the elder explained, to crowd under the exhorter's stand and engage in riotous disagreement. In an endeavor to chew each others' ears and gnaw holes in each others' hides, they had bumped their backs onto the rude floor underneath the preacher's feet, and in other ways raised a disturbance.

To prevent a repetition of this disorderly conduct on the part of the dogs, the hiding place under the stand had been made proof against all intruders by the use of stobs driven so close that not even a shadow could creep between.

It was in this long-time rendezvous of dogs that a couple of the Clary Grove gang seemed interested, as between services they strolled several times past the pulpit end of the arbor.

That evening, in the shadowy gloom cast by the arbor roof,

a couple of men might have been seen moving softly about, had the dark been closely scrutinized.

Just what they were doing was not apparent. They seemed to have a barrel close by and a long trough of some kind.

But nobody paid any attention to these quiet two. All interest was centered on Windy Batts, who in a trumpet voice was giving out the words of a song which all who knew him were certain would be sung with great unction and fervor.

He was reading the lines from a hymnbook. At the end of every second line he gave the pitch, whereupon all sang in many keys, but with united fervor:

> "Into a world of ruffians sent,
> I walk on hostile ground;
> While human bears, on slaughter bent,
> And raving wolves surround."

Between each two lines he shouted, "God have mercy on them Clary Grove sinners! Them ravening wolves! Strike them human bears down!"

Then the hymn went on:

> "The lion seeks my soul to slay,
> In some unguarded hour;
> And waits to tear his sleeping prey,
> And watches to devour."

"God save us from them Clary Grove lions that seek to devour."

The movements in the shadows just outside the arbor continued, but nobody noticed. The exhorter, calling on God and all the holy angels to witness the truth of his sayings, was drawing a graphic comparison between the righteous and the sinner, especially that most fallen and hopeless sinner—the Clary Grove sinner.

After the discourse, which was thundered out with tremendous force, the first altar-song was announced:

> If you get there before I do,
>   I'm bound for the land of Ca-na-yan;
> Look out for me, I'm coming, too,
>   I'm bound for the land of Ca-na-yan.

When this popular song got well underway, the woods for miles around rang with the refrain. The altar filled with sinners who fell in the dust, and with saints who whispered in their ears full directions for planting their feet firmly on the old ship Zion, and with shouters, among whom was Phoebe Jane Benson.

Ann Rutledge and Nance Cameron on one side of the arbor, and Abe Lincoln and Jo Kelsy on the other, had watched Phoebe Jane taking her combs out and in other ways preparing for the shouting. Ann, remembering what Mrs. Benson had said about hugging, was prepared to watch for developments as Phoebe Jane, with arms flying, began her religious exercise.

When the mourners were prostrating themselves in the dust, one of the dark figures in the shadowy background whispered, "Tickle her up and then run"; and as he reached a long pole into the enclosure under the exhorter's feet he said, "Sick 'em, kitty!" and the two were off.

Just as the first sinner was saved and the shouters were getting well warmed up, a heavy and most unreligious odor suddenly pervaded the air.

The front row of mourners, with their faces in the dust, nearest the exhorter's stand, noticed it first as it came like a puff from the infernal regions just pictured by Windy Batts. Lifting their heads, these mourners looked about, with facial expressions none too pious, to see what had smitten them. Next the shouters got the full force of the growing odor. Immediately their shouts turned to groans, and they put their hands over their noses. By this time the mourners were on their feet. This sudden change from the dust of humiliation to the erect poise of saved souls, ordinarily denoted a conversion. At this time, however, the eye of suspicion cast on every man by every other man, together with the sudden and violent outbreak of snorting and spewing, gave evidence of something different from spiritual birth.

When Windy Batts, who at this first moment was engaged in holding Phoebe Jane in the close embrace of brotherly love, was struck by the force of the permeating odor, he pushed Phoebe Jane from him, giving her a look both questioning and unsanctified.

A moment, and he understood. Springing onto his high platform, he cried in trumpet tones, "The devil is at his old game! A burning, fiery trial is about to test our faith. Sometimes afflictions come like lice, mites, boils, fits. But the worst has been reserved for these later days, and now doth God afflict his people with a skunk. Satan abounds on every hand. The most eternal and ding-blasted stink ever turned loose on the sanctuary of the Lord is now in our midst. Let a committee of fearless men with good noses volunteer to locate the spot where this varmint of the pit is hiding."

The source of the odor was soon located. About this time, out in the darkness of the woods, was heard a man's voice shouting:

> "The devil's dead.
> Oh! smell his stink;
> Killed by the power of Windy."

Then a rooster was heard crowing—the crow repeating the words. Then a cat yowled—and a dog growled—and a goose quacked—all sending out the same message about the devil's death and the manner thereof.

Here was insult added to injury, for while the exhorter might have forgiven God and the angels for the horrible ordeal they were passing through, he could never forgive the Clary Grove crowd.

During the excitement John McNeil had joined Ann Rutledge and Nance Cameron.

"It's those Clary Grove rowdies," John McNeil said. "They're a bad lot, and there will be murderers in the bunch if they do not change their ways. For this they should be put in jail."

"Windy Batts said very unkind things about them," Ann observed.

"And didn't say half bad enough. I'm sorry Abe Lincoln joined in with them. He was in their camp last night. Like as not he hatched this whole plot."

"I can't see why he should want to do a thing like that," Ann said.

"You don't? Don't you know the whole Clary Grove gang is opposed to religion? Do you suppose this rail splitter would choose their kind if he wasn't an opposer, too?"

"But he's not a rail splitter now—he's Offutt's clerk."

"He's no real clerk and never will be. Once a rail splitter, always a rail splitter."

"Maybe so, but even then, John, it's no disgrace to be an honest rail splitter—and I'm going to ask Nance if he's an opposer."

"What difference does it make to you whether he's an opposer or not?"

"I always like to think the best of everybody, John," Ann answered, "and it's an awful sin to be an opposer of religion."

CHAPTER VIII

The Test

The Clary Grove gang were gathered in council. A grave matter was to be decided and there seemed a division of opinion as to the qualifications of Abe Lincoln for becoming a member of the brotherhood. Personally no man had an unfriendly feeling. In fact some of them liked him. But there were certain qualifications which it was not certain he possessed.

The horse trade with Buck was discussed. Had he gotten the best of Buck? Several contended that he should have kept the horse and would have done so had he not been afraid of the gang. Others were of the opinion that he did not want the horse, and several declared him a good fellow for knowing where to quit joking.

There were graver considerations than this, however.

"Ever seen a man that had any guts totin' rabbits around in his pockets?" Ole Bar questioned sharply. "I seen a feller once that packed a couple of wild cats about with him—but rabbits —*rabbits*——" and language failed to express his disgust.

"And he don't drink no whiskey."

"And Jo Kelsy says he never carries a gun."

"Don't never go gamin'?"

"No," answered Jo Kelsy, "he ain't never been no hunter."

"Hain't never killed nothin'?" Ole Bar questioned in amazement.

"Not just fer fun. Once he killed a pant'er what dropped on him without saying nothin'. He ketched it around the neck and choked its eyes out and skinned it. He said he wouldn't have bothered it if it hadn't acted so nasty and climbed his frame without warnin'."

There was silence. No such case had come up for discussion. Here was a young giant who could strangle a panther—perhaps a bear. Yet he didn't bother them if they let him alone, and he carried newborn rabbits in his pocket, and didn't drink whiskey.

"Offutt's got him put up against any man in Sangamon County; says he can outrun, outwrestle, outthrow, outwhip the best man that can be put up. He's bragged till folks has forgot about Jack Armstrong of Clary Grove."

The eyes of the company turned to Jack Armstrong, the champion wrestler of Sangamon County. Built square as an ox, his mighty muscles gave the suggestion of the monarchy of muscular force. Added to his force of muscle was unusual quickness, and added to this, as the Clary Grove crowd knew, was the art of a trick that was held permissible by the gang as a last resort in holding championship of the county.

"What about it, Jack?" Kit Parsons asked.

"I'll wrastle him."

"He's different from anything you've gone up against. Jo Kelsy saw him lift a whiskey barrel and let a feller drink out of the bung hole one day when he was in the store."

"The Lord's truth," Jo answered solemnly.

"And Buck Thompson says he histed a chicken coop that weighed five or six hundred pounds and set her down on the other side of the yard, nobody lendin' a hand."

"The Lord's truth," Buck answered.

"And Ole Bar says they was having some sort of a contest down at the mill when he first come here—some sort of a stone-moving tussle—and Abe Lincoln let them strap him like a hoss and moved a thousand pounds. Hey, Ole Bar?"

"I ain't sayin' nothin', only I seen it done."

"I can whip any man on Sangamon River." It was Armstrong who spoke.

This was final and gave great satisfaction. The crowd shook hands with the champion, and one of the number was appointed to bear the challenge to Abe Lincoln, early the next morning.

When the young clerk was approached on the matter of the fight he declined. "What's the use of this wooly-rousin', anyhow? I never did see no sense in tusslin' and cuffin'. Grown-up men might be in better business."

But Offutt, satisfied that he could win the contest, urged him on, and as there seemed nothing else to do, Lincoln accepted, and the day was set.

The news spread over town and around the country. Jack Armstrong, the long-time champion, was to meet the giant youth known as Flatboat Abe, the rail splitter.

Early in the game Offutt and Bill Clary bet ten dollars on their respective men. Lesser lights bet whiskey, knives, tobacco, and even caps and coats. The better element entered no protest, and the Clary Grove kind from Wolf Creek openly exulted.

During the growing interest Lincoln seemed to pay no attention to the matter nor cared to discuss it. He said he had a good feeling for the whole bunch and believed his antagonist to be a brave and square wrestler.

"Clear the street of weak things," Bill Clary had advised, the morning of the match, which was taken to mean that there might be a gang fight instead of a wrestling match.

Even before the appointed hour the town was out and lined up opposite Offutt's store. Doctor Allen, who had formed a warm friendship for the young clerk and who was opposed to fighting, was there. The schoolteacher was there; Clary Grove to a man was present with several from Wolf Creek. James Rutledge and Cameron stopped by to look on. The women folks were on hand, for here was something that promised to be as interesting as a shouting match at a camp meeting. And the girls were there— Nance Cameron, Ann Rutledge, Phoebe Jane Benson and Ellen

Green, keyed-up with the excitement that comes to the young female of any species when the males of like kind give an exhibition of primitive strength. Nor did John McNeil remain away. He even stood by a Clary Grove leader to see the show.

Many glances were cast at the store, inside of which Abe Lincoln was seen talking to a crowd and laughing as good-naturedly as if the whole town were not feverishly waiting for him to come out and face the broad-shouldered, iron-muscled man, who as calmly awaited the event, surrounded by his friends under a tree near the side of the store.

At the appointed time Abe Lincoln came out slowly and took his way in an unhurried sort of a shamble across to the side of the store. Seeing him, Jack Armstrong emerged from his friends. The tall youth extended his hand and shook in a friendly grasp. Then he pulled off his hat and pitched it aside, opened his shirt and turned it back, hitched up his breeches, tossed back his mop of black hair—and the wrestle was on.

A cheer went up as they went the first round.

Armstrong had entered the contest with the determination of a speedy finish. He knew the art. It was evident from the beginning that Lincoln was not a skilled wrestler. Indeed he seemed only defending himself, which he did so easily that he was not given full credit for it.

Armstrong gave him some blows. They might as well have fallen on a steel trap. Lincoln gave no hard blows; evidently his intention was not to inflict harm. Through the early portion of the wrestle he was entirely good-natured. But not so with Armstrong. He was working hard. He was not making progress. His backers and friends were urging him on, while cheers sounded each time his wily antagonist escaped what seemed to be a well-directed sledge-hammer blow.

When the contest had been on some minutes, it became apparent to the crowd and to Armstrong that he must use different tactics, or the wily, good-natured Abe Lincoln would keep him fighting for a week.

Armstrong now undertook his trick.

The moment he did so, the eager crowd saw an instantaneous change in the young giant.

The good-natured expression on his face was swept aside by a wave of such anger as transformed him from a citizen into a fighter. The mild and friendly light in his gray eye made way for a fire that gave it a strange, shining appearance. The slight stoop of the body disappeared and the tall figure towered high and tense for a passing instant. Then he threw out his powerful arm and just as his antagonist hoped to take him from his feet, he felt his neck caught in the grasp of something as unrelenting as a steel trap. Tighter the powerful fingers wrapped about his neck. He felt himself forced away from the man he would defeat by trickery.

It was done in a moment. The crowd saw Abe Lincoln holding Jack Armstrong at arm's length and shaking him as a cat would shake a kitten, as he shouted in white wrath, "Play fair, will ye? If you win, *win*. If you lose, *lose—but do it like a man!* Play fair, will ye?" and again he shook him as if in an effort to shake the words from him.

For a moment there was an ominous silence.

"He's a bar! He's a bar!" shouted Ole Bar. Whatever this meant was uncertain. The gang closed in. They seemed coming to the rescue of their champion.

With the breath half-choked out of him, Armstrong felt himself pulled along. Abe Lincoln backed against the store wall. He released Armstrong, shouting, "I'm ready! I'll meet anybody in a fair tussle, but no tricks go with Abe Lincoln!"

Again there was a moment of silence. The gang looked at Armstrong, then the crowd cheered. The gang fell back. The next moment something unexpected happened. Jack Armstrong approached, held out his hand and, turning to the crowd, said, "Boys, Abe Lincoln's the best fellow that ever broke into this gang."

The white anger faded from the face of the tall giant as quickly as it had come. The fire passed from his eyes. His homely face was lit by a kindly smile. He hitched up his trousers and pushed back his hair. Then with his hand warmly grasped around that of Armstrong he said, "Hand-shakes are better than cuffin's. It's friends we are."

A shout went up, the women shouting with the men. Among those who cheered most heartily was the group of girls with whom Ann Rutledge stood. So interested had she been in the climax of the contest that she had not noticed that John McNeil had moved to a place beside her. She did not know it until, in the midst of her most enthusiastic hand-clapping, she turned and met his eye. Her face was bright with pleasure at the outcome. She was laughing and cheering. When she met his eye she knew he was not pleased.

"I told you he'd be one of the gang," McNeil said.

"But he plays fair."

"I never could understand why women and girls like the fighting kind, the rowdy kind—the kind that has roustabout ways, and that has no business, and opposes religion."

"But are you sure he opposes religion?"

"These fighting roustabouts generally do. Now don't get mixed. I'm not saying Abe Lincoln's not a good fellow. He's good enough of his kind, and I like him. But for women and girls that's religious, he wouldn't be my kind."

"I'm going to find out if he opposes religion," Ann said.

"Going over to the store to see him?" John questioned.

"No; I would so like to talk with him just once. But I won't because——"

"Why?" he asked, looking at her.

"Because, John, some way I feel you would not like it. I'm promised to you, and I play fair."

He made no answer, but some way Ann felt that her statement was not altogether satisfactory to John McNeil.

Thou Shalt Not Covet

The wrestling match that proved the championship of Sangamon River established Abe Lincoln, with his love of peace and his unlimited reserve of physical power to enforce it, as the peace-maker of New Salem.

The following day James Rutledge called at the store.

James Rutledge, with his partner Cameron, was the founder of New Salem. Some few years before, he had come from Kentucky with his family, bought a farm a few miles to the west, built a mill at New Salem, and opened a store and a tavern.

Within a year, ten log houses had been added to the original two. A cobbler and a blacksmith had shops. Then a few more houses were built and a cooper mill where crude barrels and kegs were made.

James Rutledge, a descendant of the famous Rutledge family of the Carolinas, possessed the manly qualities of his ancestors in full measure, and pioneer life had by no means obliterated those instincts which make generous friends and progressive citizens.

Mr. Rutledge was also a firm believer in education as the foundation for the future greatness of the new Western country as well as the success of the individual, and it was largely due to his efforts that the Scotch schoolmaster, Mentor Graham was among the first settlers.

James Rutledge had been into the new store before to look around. Once he had tarried to hear a story. But he was a busy man and had as yet formed no special acquaintance with the much-discussed Abe Lincoln.

This visit was for the purpose of getting acquainted. After Rutledge had warmly congratulated the ungainly clerk on his insistence on fair play, they sat down to talk, and the conversation turned to a discussion of the widely renowned circuit rider Peter Cartwright, who was expected to hold a wonderful meeting in the vicinity of Springfield during the month of September.

Abe Lincoln had heard of Peter Cartwright, the eccentric Methodist exhorter, who was born in a Kentucky canebrake and rocked in a bee-gum cradle, and could tell many stories about himself.

The outcome of this short visit was an invitation to the clerk to visit Rutledge Inn and tell some of the Cartwright stories.

Rutledge Inn was the largest building in the town except the mill. None of the other homes had more than two rooms, some only one. Rutledge Inn had four rooms and a sort of porch made by an extension of the roof over a hardly packed, cleanly swept, dirt floor. It was here where Mentor Graham, Dr. Allen, James Rutledge, William Green and others of the intelligent citizens gathered to discuss news, matters of education, religion and politics.

Quite pleased with his invitation, Abe Lincoln went to the inn and found, in addition to the family, Mentor Graham and Dr. Allen.

It was a night in late August. The stars twinkled above the dark outlines of the trees that crested the bluff. The one road of New Salem, that wound its way down the hill, lay like a gray ribbon, and log houses made the darker spots that at irregular intervals marked it. Occasionally, the call of a night bird sent ripples of melody onto the stillness, or sometimes the tinkle of a bell stirred the ocean of the night silence, while the fall of the dam water sent out its rhythm in never ending cadences.

The discussion turned to religion, a most fruitful topic of argument, for Mentor Graham was a Hard Shell and Dr. Allen was a Predestinarian. This night there was the uncommon Abe Lincoln to be heard from. Stories of Peter Cartwright were first on the program, and from these the conversation turned to a discussion of religion in particular and its uses to mankind.

"One of the best uses of religion," Dr. Allen said, "is to cast out fear. Medicine won't work when fear is present and there's been many a man scared to death. I was called out once to see a child who had been bitten by a rattlesnake. She died and her father nearly lost his mind. Later he got bit in the night by something—a spider, I think. He was sure it was a rattlesnake. There was no need of the man dying, but he did die—actually *frightened to death*. It's an awful condition for a soul to be in that fears eternal punishment for sin. Religion takes away this fear."

"Just what is religion?" asked Abe Lincoln. "From what I've been able to gather, it's preachin' purgatory and damnation till you get up a panic, offerin' the mercy of God as a way of escape, and then takin' up a collection for the good advice you have given—is this religion?"

The men laughed.

"I may be off," Lincoln continued, "but looks to me like there wouldn't be so much need of gettin' the fear out of folks if the fear of hell wasn't first preached into them."

"Don't you believe in hell?" Mentor Graham asked.

"Can't say I do."

"But you believe in God, I am sure."

"Yes—only a fool has said in his heart there is no God."

"But the same authority that teaches God teaches hell," Dr. Allen said.

"Not to my way of thinking—it don't," Lincoln answered. "'The heavens declare the glory of God and the firmament shows his handiwork,' the Book tells me. But I can't see how the heavens declare the glory of hell nor its necessity either."

"But how can God punish the unrighteous without a hell? Can't you see that by taking hell out of the Bible you destroy its value as an inspired book, and where else can one learn of God?"

"Have you forgotten the heavens and the stars? And then there are other things, too, besides the Bible, that tell of God. Did you ever watch a mud dauber? Know how he works, do you? Builds his nest and puts in his egg. The young one is not goin' to get out until it can fly, so it must have food. The parent goes in search. Here comes a worm. Good food and enough to last until the young dauber is ready to wing its way. But there is a difficulty. If the dauber kills the worm and puts it in, it will be rotten as heck before the young is ready to get out. What happens? The dauber sticks its stinger into a certain spot where it paralyzes the worm—knocks him out, so to speak, without killin' him. Then he puts him in the cell with the young, seals him and leaves. What I say is—where does the mud dauber get his knowledge? Who told him to deaden that food without killin' it? Who shows him, or her, just the right point to stick in that sting? To me it has always seemed that any Creator that can plan this way has more than horse sense. But to make folks, like the Book says, in his own likeness and image, and then get mad at them and roast them alive a million or so years 'cause they can't swallow Hard Shell religion, or gulp down Predestinarianism, looks like God hain't planned things as well as a mud dauber. Maybe I'm lackin' myself, but I got to turn loose of God or hell one, and for my purpose I'm choosin' to hang on to God, and I somehow got a feelin' he's not goin' back on me. 'Twouldn't be fair—and God plays fair, gentlemen—God plays fair."

There was a moment of silence. Then James Rutledge said, "Davy, get a jug from the cellar. Sis, bring the water pitcher, glasses and sugar."

As the boy and girl arose Lincoln turned slightly. He had not noticed before that the daughter of the house had joined the group.

As he saw her now in the semidarkness she looked like some fair creature of another world. He had heard that Ann Rutledge was the prettiest girl in town. She had passed his store and been pointed out to him. He had been told she was engaged to marry John McNeil who was the most settled young fellow in town and already worth ten thousand dollars. But neither of these news items had interested him sufficiently to take his attention from the story he had happened to be telling or hearing when she had passed.

As his eyes turned toward her, he saw she was leaning forward as if not to lose a word, and gazing at him intently.

He changed the glance of his eye to give her a chance to look another way. Then he turned his glance on her again. As he did so, there came to him a revelation. Here was the pilgrim. How did he know it? He could not tell; yet, as surely as she sat there in the dim light, as surely as his eyes were resting on her golden head and fair face, he knew it.

Mentor Graham and Dr. Allen had launched a spirited discussion on baptism. Abe Lincoln did not join them. He turned his eyes again toward the girl. In the half-light he could not see the expression of her face, but her face was turned toward him and he was conscious she was thinking of him. She turned away as if embarrassed, but no sooner had he shifted than the dark eyes again turned toward the heroic figure, a figure like a bronze, the profile of his face half-Roman and half-Indian. His head rested on a neck of cords and muscles which stood straight out from a turn-down collar.

As irresistible as the pole draws the magnet, the glances of the two were drawn toward each other again, and in the dark each felt the meeting of this glance. Then Ann Rutledge got up and went away.

Abe Lincoln thought of the bird he had heard the night he sat on the ladder—the night the voice had called to him from the heights. He smiled.

The next morning Abe Lincoln was at the store early, waiting to see McNeil pass. When he had heard half a dozen times before that Ann Rutledge was engaged to marry McNeil, the words had been as idle gossip. Nor had he given McNeil any special attention. Now all was different. With keen eye and feverish desire he waited to pass judgment.

As the young man passed, the watching Lincoln felt himself moved by some tremendous impulse of destruction, a destruction that would annihilate this man from the face of the earth as completely as though he had never existed.

As he stood in the doorway of the rude frontier store, no Sinaitic thunder roared its disapproval of this primitive animal impulse. But he heard, instead, the gentle voice of a woman who had long lain sleeping under the tangle of a forsaken wildwood— a voice that had read to him from an open book by the light of a pine torch fire, "Thou shalt not covet."

CHAPTER X

The Mysterious Pig

One day a poverty-stricken and dispirited woman, whom Abe Lincoln had not before seen, entered his store to buy a few candles and a small quantity of molasses.

As she went out, the storekeeper was informed that she was the wife of a notorious drunkard, known throughout the settlement as Snoutful Kelly, who lived in a miserable shack out near Muddy Point.

After the woman had gone, in casting up his accounts, Abe Lincoln found himself with a few pennies more than he should have, and, after puzzling over the small excess, he discovered that he had overcharged the wife of Snoutful Kelly.

Though it was yet early, he closed the store and at once set out toward Muddy Point to return the woman's change.

The shack he found the family living in was not the worst he had even seen, and he himself had once lived in one nearly as bad. He had not expected, however, to find such a home near the thrifty settlement of New Salem.

The hearth was of dirt with a hole in the middle made by much sweeping. There was a puncheon table with forked sticks for legs, and wooden trenchers for plates. Sharp pieces of cane were used for forks; there was one knife without a handle, and one tin cup for the use of the entire family. In one corner was a pallet of leaves on a post frame with a thin quilt over it.

When Abe Lincoln entered the one room he found the mother bending over the hearth, and a small girl, with a black eye, trying to quiet a dirty baby which kicked on the post bed.

At a first glance Lincoln saw that the woman was in trouble, and, while she thanked him in a crude way for the return of the pennies and took them eagerly, her mind was thus only partially diverted from the trouble.

Hungry for pity, and led to believe she might get it from this tall youth who had come so far to return her change, the woman poured out her tale of woe.

Her pig was gone—her only pig—the pig which the children had divided food with that they might have a bit of meat for the winter. Her husband would not fix the pen and the pig had escaped and gone some days before. The bitter loss was too much for the poor woman, and she broke down and wept.

Moved with pity, Abe Lincoln asked what kind of pig it was.

"Black, with a white spot on its left shank, and a white eye, and its ear was fresh cut with two slits and a cross mark—like this," and bending over the hearth she made some marks in the ashes which Lincoln looked at carefully. "I suppose some wolf or cat smelled the blood, 'cause nobody would steal a pig in these parts, would they?" There was appeal in her voice as she asked the question.

Further discussion about the pig was cut off by a screech from the child, whose face suddenly took on an expression of great fear, while her eyes seemed fixed in horror on something she saw coming toward the house.

Abe Lincoln glanced out.

"It's her pap coming," the woman explained. "He beat her somethin' fearful yesterday 'cause she got in the mud. And he told her he'd throw her in up to her neck today if she got in the mud, and let her stick there till the buzzards eat 'er up. And how is the poor child to help it when her pap has brought her here where there ain't nothing but mud to fall in?" Then, turning to the child, she said: " 'Tain't no use to have fits. Nobody but God can keep him from gittin' ye."

"Nobody but God, eh?" Abe Lincoln said. "We'll see."

The man came staggering toward the house, cursing and growling, his drunken wrath seeming to center itself on the child whose face was transfixed with terror.

The child screamed just as he was about to enter the house to make good his threats. Then there suddenly pounced upon him, from just inside, something that caught him in a grip like that of a vise, and pulled him back outside. And then this something, which was a very tall youth, began shaking him and slowly making his way, as he did so, toward the creek.

As a result of the none too gentle shaking, the liquid matter the drunkard had imbibed began to return to the world of visible things until what seemed an endless amount had been emptied along the way they were taking. When the burden of liquor had been lightened, the drunkard, now chattering for pity, was ducked in the stream until his dripping chin was washed clean, and his thick tongue limbered up.

He was then marched back to the cabin door, from which the wife, and the child with a black eye, looked out in speechless wonder.

"Here you are now," said the tall man. "My name is Abe Lincoln. I keep store in town. I can get here in twenty minutes any time I'm needed to break up this child-beatin'—understand?" and he was off.

It was that same night Abe Lincoln dropped down to Clary's Grove, where he was now always welcome. When he arrived he found a feast in course of preparation. A pig was roasting in the fire and the savory odor permeated the air as different ones of the gang poked the fire, basted the roast, and otherwise prepared for the occasion.

"Just in time, my son, Abry Linkhorn," said Ole Bar.

"Where'd you get that pig?" Lincoln inquired,

"It lit in a tree and we clubbed it out and picked it. 'Tain't none too fat, but it'll do."

"Let me look at its ears," Lincoln said. "Two slits and a cross," he observed. Then he told the story of Snoutful Kelly's wife and her great grief at the loss of the pig.

There was a moment of impressive silence. Then one of the gang said: "Clary's Grove has done some things that hain't been written in no book, but they don't steal from no weepin' wimmin, and beat up hungry children. As good a pig must be put back in that pen as was ever caught in the woods by the wolves and cats."

This speech expressed the sentiment of the company, and a game was played to see who would replace the pig. When this had been decided, they returned to their feast with consciences apparently as clear as those of children.

It was the second day following the feast by the Clary Grove boys that Ann Rutledge missed one of her pigs. Ann was not only a famous needle woman, a spinner, and a cook, but she had good luck raising pigs and chickens, and her father gave her a pig or two in each litter, which were to be her own to help in getting her education.

Now her pig was gone—a black one with a white spot on its flank.

Mounted on one of James Rutledge's good horses, Ann set out to search the woods for her pig.

She had gotten some distance without finding any trace of it, when she heard the cry of a child. Following the direction from which the sound came, she soon discovered a forlorn little specimen of a girl, with a black and purple eye, who was looking about in different directions as if not knowing which way to go, and was crying.

"What's the matter?" asked Ann Rutledge. "Are you lost?"

"Yes," the child answered.

"Who are you—and where do you live?"

"I'm Katy Kelly, and I live at Muddy Point. Our pig is lost

again," she sobbed. "We got it home once, but the pen broke, and now it's gone again."

"I'm looking for a pig, too," Ann said. "Get up on my horse, and we'll look a little and then I'll take you home."

The child climbed on, and the search continued. But the child no longer had eyes for anything but Ann Rutledge.

"How did you hurt your eye?" Ann asked kindly.

"Pap, he did it. He bunged me with his fist. He said he'd git me again the same way, and stick me in the mud till the buzzards picked my eyes out. I was scared to death. It's horrible to get bunged and beat. I begged Mam to keep Pap from beatin' me again, but he beats her, too, and she said nobody but God could keep him from beatin' me up. Just as he was about to git me, here comes God with the longest legs on earth, and he reached out his long arms an' got Pap and shook all the red eye out of him he's poured in fer a year. Then he ducked him until he got sobered up. Mam says Pap won't beat me no more, she'll bet on it, 'cause God—He can git anywhere on them legs, in twenty minutes."

This story was told between snubs and sobs, and the dirty dress sleeve was called into use between sentences to dry the tearful eyes and dripping nose.

Ann Rutledge was interested.

"So God came to help you?"

"Yep—his name is Abe Lincoln—he told Pap."

"Abe Lincoln!" Ann exclaimed. Then she rode a long way without speaking. She was thinking. The name brought the picture of a strong, elemental man, seemingly older than his years, a man who had said he was going to play fair with God, a man whom Nance Cameron had pronounced the homeliest creature that God ever put breath in.

"There's home," the child presently said, "and, *there's the pig.*"

Ann looked. A small black pig with a white spot on its flank. She knew the pig.

But when she dismounted to examine the pig she found its ear cut with two slits and a cross.

"We found it in the pen. At first I couldn't believe it," Mrs. Kelly exclaimed. "It looked a bit fatter than mine, but it's ear was fresh marked; I cut it myself. And I thanked God it had come back."

"You thanked God," Ann observed as if to herself.

"Yes—for it's our only winter meat. And when it got out again, I was sick over it—and likely it will get away some more, for Kelly never in his life fixed a pen that would hold."

"I'll help you fix the pen," Ann said, and she did, meantime wondering about the pig, for she would have sworn it was her own.

CHAPTER XI

Peter Cartwright Arrives

It was on a September day that the famous Peter Cartwright jogged into New Salem on a stiff-legged pony, and drew up before Rutledge Inn.

His visit had been long expected and great preparations had been made for the camp meeting which was to be held in the Springfield district in a few days.

No announcement had been made of the time Peter Cartwright would arrive, yet in that mysterious way that news spreads over a small town, even while he was yet removing the saddle bags from his tired pony, sightseers had congregated on the opposite side of the street, and before sundown everybody in town knew that the great preacher was stopping for the night at Rutledge Inn.

Abe Lincoln had been invited to the inn, with the select few who often made the little party, to meet the Reverend Mr. Peter Cartwright. They met a rather small, wiry man with bright foxlike eyes, and hair inclined to be curly, which stood out in every direction on a round head.

He talked freely, criticizing in no unmeasured terms such preachers as preach not against slavery, dram-drinking, dancing, or the putting on of costly apparel and jewelry. Then with a twinkle in his small, bright eye, he said that his risibilities were often hard to keep down owing to some things that happened as he traveled his circuit, and he told them an incident:

"I rode one day into Springfield to transact a little business. My horse had at one time been an excellent pony, but now had the stiff complaint. I stopped for a few moments into a store to purchase a few articles, and I saw in the store a young lady in company with two young men; we were perfect strangers; they soon passed out and rode off. After transacting my business I left the store, mounted my stiff pony, and set out for home. After riding some distance, I saw just ahead of me a two-horse wagon, with the cover rolled up. It was warm weather, and I saw in the wagon those two young men and the young lady that I had seen in the store. As I drew near them they began to sing one of our camp-meeting songs, and they appeared to sing with great animation. Presently the young lady began to shout, and said, 'Glory to God! Glory to God!' The driver cried out, 'Amen, Glory to God!'

"My first impressions were that they had been across the Sangamon River to a camp meeting that I knew was in progress there, and had obtained religion, and were happy. As I drew a little nearer, the young lady began to sing and shout again. The young man who was not driving fell down and cried aloud for mercy; the other two, shouting at the top of their voices, cried out, 'Glory to God! another sinner's down.' Then they began to exhort the young man that was down, saying, 'Pray on, brother; pray on, brother; you will soon get religion'; and up jumped the young man that was down, shouting aloud, saying, 'God has blessed my soul. Hallelujah! Hallelujah! Glory to God!'

"Thinking all was right, I felt like riding up and joining in the songs of triumph and shouts of joy that rose from these three happy persons. But, as I neared the wagon, I saw them cast glances at each other and at me, and I suspected then that they were making a mock of religious things, and, knowing me to be a preacher, wished to fool me. I stopped my horse and fell back, and rode slowly, thinking they would ride on, and so not annoy me any more; but when I checked my horse and went slow, they slackened their pace and went slow too, and the driver changed places with the other young man. Then they began to sing and shout at a furious rate and down fell the first driver, and up went a new shout of 'Glory to God! another sinner's down. Pray on, brother; pray on, brother; the Lord will bless you.' Presently up sprang the driver, saying, 'Glory to God! He has blessed me.' And both the others shouted and said, 'Another sinner's converted, another sinner's converted. Hallelujah! Glory to God!' A rush of indignant feeling came all over me, and I felt as if I wanted to ride up and horsewhip both of these rowdies, and if a lady had not been present I might have done so, but, as it was, I did not. It was a vexatious encounter; if my horse had been fleet, as in former days, I could have rode right off and left them in their glory, but he was stiff, and when I would fall back and go slow, they would check up; and when I would spur my stiff pony and try to get ahead of them they would crack the whip and keep ahead of me; and thus they tormented me until my patience was entirely exhausted. They kept up a continual roar of 'Another sinner's down! Another soul's converted! Glory to God! Pray on, brother! Hallelujah! Hallelujah! Glory to God!' and I felt it was more than any good minister ought to bear.

"I cannot describe my feelings at this time. It seemed that I was delivered over to be tormented by the devil and his imps. Just at this moment I thought of a terrible mud hole about a quarter of a mile ahead. It was a long and very deep mud, and many teams had stuck in it, and had to be pried out. Near the center of this mud hole there was a place of mud deeper than anywhere else. On the right stood a stump about two feet high; all the wagons had to be driven close to this stump so as to avoid a deep rut on the left, where many wagons had stuck. I knew where there was a small bridle way that wound round through the brush to avoid the mud, and the thought occurred to me that, when we came up to this muddy place, I would take the bridle way, and put my horse at the top of his speed and by so doing get away from these miserable tormentors, as I knew they could not drive fast through this long plot of mud. When we drove near to the commencement of the mud I took the bridle path, and put spurs and whip to my horse. Perceiving that I was rapidly leaving them in the rear, their driver cracked his whip, and put his horses at almost full speed, and such was their anxiety to keep up with me to carry out their sport that, when they came to this bad place, they never saw the stump on the right. The fore wheel of the wagon struck centrally on the stump, and as the wheel mounted the stump over went the wagon. Fearing it would turn entirely over and catch them under, the two young men took a leap into the mud, and when they lighted they sunk up to their middle. The young lady was dressed in white, and as the wagon went over, she sprang as far as she could, and lighted on all fours, her hands sunk into the mud up to her armpits, her mouth and the whole of her face immersed in the muddy water, and she certainly would have strangled if one of the young men had not relieved her. I rode up to the edge of the mud, stopped my horse, reared in my stirrups and shouted at the top of my voice, 'Glory to God! Glory to God! Hallelujah! Another sinner's down! Glory to God! Hallelujah! Glory! Hallelujah!'

"If ever youngsters felt mean those did; and well they might, for they had carried on all this sport to make light of religion, and to insult a minister, a total stranger to them. But they contemned religion, and hated Methodists, especially Methodist preachers.

"When I became tired of shouting over them, I said to them, 'Now you poor, dirty, mean sinners, take this as a just judgment of God upon you for your meanness, and repent of your dreadful wickedness; and let this be the last time that you attempt to insult a preacher; for if you repeat your abominable sport and persecutions, the next time God will serve you worse, and the devil will get you.'

"They felt so badly that they never uttered one word of reply.

Now I was very glad that I did not horsewhip them, as I felt like doing; but that God had avenged His own cause, and defended His own honor without my doing it with carnal weapons. Later, at one of my prosperous camp meetings, I had the great pleasure to see all three of these young people converted to God, and I took them into the Methodist Church." *

Cartwright's mission was not, however, storytelling, as was soon made evident. "Time is bearing on us," he said, "toward the Judgment. Are we prepared? *This* is the question—it is the *one great* question. Brethren and sisters, is every soul here prepared to meet his God? Let me see." There was a general indication that those present were. Abe Lincoln did not signify readiness. "We are going to pray," Cartwright said, "and you, my young friend," addressing him, "should humble yourself and call to God for deliverance from hell, for surely the enemy of man's soul is on his track, and damnation is the eternal punishment of the unsaved. Fear hell and flee to God."

"But I don't fear hell," Abe Lincoln said comfortably.

"Don't fear hell?" There was both condemnation and surprise in Cartwright's tone as he repeated the words. "By such unbelief you question the existence of God."

"No—I don't question the existence of God, but I would if I believed eternal damnation. You see, parson, you and me don't measure God by the same yardstick."

"But to doubt hell is to doubt God. The same inspired book is the authority for both."

"For some, maybe, but not for others. Old Snoutful Kelly brought a child into the world without never once askin' her whether she wanted to come or not. Then he moved her to Muddy Point where there was nothin' but mud, without askin' her if she wanted to go. Then he told her to keep out of the mud, and when she couldn't he gave her a black eye. Having knocked her blind, he told her if she got into the mud again he'd 'souse her in a mud hole to her ears and leave her there

* From *Autobiography of Peter Cartwright*.

for the buzzards to pick her eyes out.' Now you say God brings us here children into this world without askin' nothin' about it, where there's devilment all about us, and we didn't put that here, either. Then you have God give us a black eye with this original sin you preach about, which makes us sin whether we want to or not, and when He gets us He promises hell fire and eternal damnation for gettin' into sin. This here don't sound like God to me. It sounds like Snoutful Kelly."

The silence that followed this statement was the kind that seems reduced to pound weight. Cartwright stared at the presumptuous youth who had uttered such words. When he could speak, he said: "Coming from the lips of a worm of the dust, I should call such sacrilege—nothing short of blasphemy."

"Might be true if I counted myself among worms, but I don't. I may look like a worm, Brother Cartwright, or a pair of worms, or even four worms of the dust tied together, but I haven't none of that wormy feelin' you hint at, and I don't take stock in wormy religion. The Good Book is full of more upliftin' texts than the wormy ones. I'd forget about hell fire and worms of the dust for a while if I was a preacher."

"What would you preach, Abe?" Mentor Graham asked.

"Want to know, do you?"

"Yes—yes," the answer was given by both Rutledge and Dr. Allen.

Lincoln arose. For a moment he seemed slouchy, bent, and ill at ease. Then he straightened up and announced his text, " 'Beloved, now are ye the sons of God, and it does not yet appear what we shall be.' "

As he spoke, a wonderful change came over him. His face lit up, his gestures grew natural and strong, his voice, thin-sounding at first, took on melody, his ill-fitting clothing was forgotten. He seemed for the moment lifted away from his surroundings, and those listening were lifted with him.

As he reached the end of his brief speech and declared, " 'And every man that hath this hope in him, purifieth himself,' " he was measuring up to some far heights.

When he finished his short sermon he stood a few seconds. Then his shoulders drooped, the bright spark faded from his eye and gave place to the quiet, almost dull gray, and a quizzical smile softened his face as he said, in sitting down, "Let those who feel like worms be as decent as they can. Let those that feel themselves sons of God go forward toward better things. Isn't this the Scripture, Brother Cartwright?"

The small, bright eyes of the great exhorter were fastened on the face of the homely youth. Here evidently was a specimen whose like he had not seen.

"There be those," answered Cartwright, "who wrest the Scriptures to their own damnation. We were created sons of God to be sure. But we have been separated by the fall of Adam and eternally lost unless we return to the fold by the one way."

"That's just it, which is the right way? Dr. Allen here goes by the Predestinarian gate. Graham goes by the Hard Shell gate. The New Lights have their way, the Free Wills theirs, the Dunkards and the Shakers have theirs, and you choose the shouting Methodist way. Which of them all is right?"

"Right—Why, *I am right*, as I can prove by the Scriptures." Lincoln laughed.

"Come to hear me preach and I can *prove* to you that I am right. You're tall and mighty in your own opinion, but I've seen the tall and lofty sons of Belial bite the dust. Come to hear me! I'll get the scales from your eyes and the stiffness out of your knees. Let us pray. To your knees, people," and with fervid honesty and all his consecrated lung power, the great exhorter called on *all*-mighty God to have mercy on the self-satisfied sinner in their midst.

CHAPTER XII

The Righteous Shout

The meeting which Peter Cartwright was to hold had been heralded far and wide, and it was expected that several thousand people would attend. A great arbor had been erected at each of the four corners of which was a high wooden altar covered with earth and sod where pine torches burned to illuminate the darkness. A platform large enough to hold twenty preachers had been built, with an open space in front scattered with straw and lined with mourners' benches. Back from the arbor a circle of tents was placed; back of the tents, wagons, buggies, and carts of every description; and back of this rim of vehicles the horses, and sometimes oxen, were tethered.

The gathering together of so many people from far and near for a period of two or three weeks offered an opportunity for profit-making, and at a previous meeting whiskey as well as cider and tobacco had been sold in the forest beyond the camp clearing, and wheels of chance had been operated, all of which had had a bad effect on the meeting.

The Clary Grove boys, after a report from Lincoln, had decided to "give Old Pete right of way," and planned neither mischief nor profit-making.

Not so, however, the Wolf Creek and Sand Town gangs; some among these had decided to use the occasion for money-making, and the day before the meeting was to open, several barrels of whiskey were discovered in the brush down beyond the camp arbor.

Cartwright immediately sent out word that no whiskey-selling would be allowed anywhere near the meeting ground, and to the end of discovering whom he must fight, he disguised himself and was thus able to locate the gang of rowdies whose headquarters he found a short distance down a little creek running by the camp ground. Close to the arbor was a steep bank, below which the water was quite deep. Peter Cartwright learned that a plan had been made to throw him into this pool. The rowdies were then to ride through the arbor on horses and with screeches and yells like those of Indians, break up the meeting.

With this information in hand, Peter Cartwright prepared himself and, armed with a stout hickory club, he hid at the narrow passage through which the horsemen were to come, a pathway around the high bank just above the deep pool.

The singing service which preceded the sermon, led by the ten exhorters up at the arbor, was swelling into an inspiring volume when Cartwright, hiding in the gloom, heard the sound of horses, and the next moment the leader of the Wolf Creek gang appeared, making his smiling way, with his eye fixed on the arbor.

It was at this time the music of the pious song was pierced by an unearthly screech, ending with the words, "In the name of the Lord, *get back!*" The horse was the first to heed the exhorter's summary order. Pitching his rider off perilously close to the brink of the creek, he snorted away into the forest.

"In the name of the Lord, get thee behind me, Satan!" Cartwright shouted again, this time into the ear of the Wolf Creek rowdy, and, with the words, he gave him such a resounding whack with his club as to knock him over the bank. The next moment the leader of the gang found himself kicking in the cold waters into which he had planned to throw Cartwright.

Several others of the gang now came up and made an effort to pass, but the yells of Cartwright had summoned the strong ones from the arbor, and after a general mixing up between the sheep and the goats, the more valiant members of the Wolf Creek gang found themselves crawling out of the water at the foot of the bank.

When the gang had been dispersed, Peter Cartwright, puffing and blowing, returned to the arbor and sounded the great trumpet call to preaching. The disturbed audience gathered in quickly, the women seating themselves on one side and the men on the other.

Taking a timely text, the exhorter described with great power the conflict he had just been having with the devil, and when he had reached the climax of the great fight, and had described the way the devil went splashing into the pool, he sprang from his pulpit to a long bench across the altar, and, walking back and forth, shouted in a mighty voice:

> Then my soul mounted higher
> In a chariot of fire,
> And the moon, it was under my feet!

From a shout the words grew into a song, improvised scriptural texts serving for the verses, and the chorus each time being the victorious statement that his soul had mounted up until the moon was under his feet. The audience soon caught the swing of the chorus and sent out great volumes of melody on the night air.

After this song, the old favorite, "Where, O where are the Hebrew children?" was started, and as the questions "Where, O where now is good Elijah?"; "Where, O where now is good old Daniel?"; "Where, O where now is my good mother?" were sung, with their answers, enthusiasm grew until the united answers rolled away in great sound waves on the stillness of the black forest.

The situation was growing interesting. There was a suppressed feeling that something was going to happen.

Among the hundreds who stood about the sides were Abe
Lincoln and Dr. Allen, who had taken the time to ride over in
the hopes of seeing for themselves an exhibit of spiritual power
known as the jerks. The perceptible and steady rise in excitement gave promise of almost any kind of unusual demonstration.
Sinners had been called to the altar and many were falling in
the dust, groaning and calling on God to save them from sin
and its terrible punishment of hell.

Cartwright by now seemed to be singing, exhorting, preaching and praying all at the same time. The shouters had felt the
power, and added to the singing and praying. Shrill cries of
"Glory," and other ejaculations of unearthly joy were heard.
Bonnets, caps, and combs were beginning to fly. Several of the
sisters gave exhibitions of what were called running, jumping
and barking exercises, and the men most interested in them were
near at hand to catch them when they fell. Some who succumbed
to this excess of joy, remained in a trancelike condition, however,
and there were at one time many unconscious men and women
lying prostrate in the straw at one place. Abe Lincoln and Dr.
Allen looked on with much interest.

In the midst of the excitement, there came to the ears of Abe
Lincoln, from the woman's side, somewhere across from him,
a familiar note. His interest was at once centered in discovering
the owner of the voice. After a very short time he saw Ann
Rutledge. Tonight she wore a dress half wool, half flax, a soft
material, dyed with butternut until it was as yellow as her
hair. She stood not far from one of the pine-torch fires, and in
the reflection of the orange flames she made a picture worthy of
an artist's canvas.

With his eyes upon her face, shining as if touched by fire
from some heavenly altar, Abe Lincoln suddenly became oblivious of the scenes about him, though proving of such unusual
interest to Dr. Allen.

The song about the Hebrew children had given way to another and yet more emotional expression: a hand-shaking ditty
which seemed little more than a monophonic impromptu to carry

the line, "My brother, I wish you well; when my Lord calls, I trust you will be mentioned in the Promised Land." Before the many improvised verses of this chant, alike rousing and pathetic, had been sung twice, the climax joy of the safety of heavenly bliss, and the climax sorrow of the doom of eternal punishment had been reached, and it was evident to Dr. Allen that the strange physical expression was about to break out.

"Look!" he said to Abe Lincoln.

There was no response.

"Look!" he repeated.

Then he glanced at the man by his side. Abe Lincoln was looking, but not as Dr. Allen had indicated, and the expression on his face was one Dr. Allen had never seen there. For a moment his eyes rested on the uncouth and homely youth in surprise; then, as if hesitating to break some pleasant spell, he took him by the arm and said softly, "They're getting the jerks."

Abe Lincoln turned suddenly, and in something of an apologetic tone said, "It's Ann Rutledge singing. Look at her face. Doesn't she seem happy?"

"Ann Rutledge is always happy," Dr. Allen answered, "but look up in front."

"Hope she don't catch it," he said with a last glance at Ann as he turned his attention to a woman who had just shaken her apron off.

"Don't fear," Dr. Allen replied smiling. "Book learning and this sort of thing don't go together."

Dr. Allen and Abe Lincoln pushed nearer the front. According to Cartwright the jerks were useful to call attention to the power of God or the devil, whichever caused the peculiar demonstration. At any rate it affected them powerfully, and soon many about the altar were in different stages of the mysterious visitation of the supernatural. The heads of some jerked from side to side. Others bent back and forth. Sometimes the whole body jerked so violently it soon fell exhausted, and many bodies that fell into the straw lay for days before returning to consciousness.

As Dr. Allen and Abe Lincoln watched, they saw one man, who stood near a support, beat against it until the skin was scraped from his forehead. Dr. Allen moved with professional pity, but Abe Lincoln said, "He's getting religion, let him alone."

It was four o'clock in the morning, when those who had breath enough left sang, "Blest be the tie that binds," and repaired to their tents to rest until the trumpet should summon them to early morning prayers.

The next morning, as Abe Lincoln and Dr. Allen were crossing the arbor grounds, they saw Ann Rutledge and John McNeil laughing together as she fried eggs over an open fire. For a moment Lincoln felt the same sensation he experienced when once before he would have destroyed McNeil from the face of the earth.

Dr. Allen noted the momentary expression on his face and involuntarily compared it with what he had seen there the night before. He did not stop now to make deductions, but he did not forget.

A little later Abe Lincoln met Ann and the Reverend Peter Cartwright. "We were talking about you," Ann said.

"I was wondering if the demonstration of Divine power at last night's meeting had not shaken the scales from your eyes, my sinner friend," was the exhorter's greeting.

"I suppose you call me a sinner because I do not believe in hell," Abe Lincoln said, smiling.

"No man can be religious and not fear hell."

"My sin then is in lack of fear, but I didn't make myself, and God just forgot to put it in. Am I to blame for that?"

"Don't be a scoffer," was Cartwright's advice. "You have a soul worth saving, young man. I shall pray for your never dying soul. Perhaps others are praying for you, and the effectual fervent prayer of the righteous man availeth much."

"Thanks. I'll do as much for you if you ever get in need," Abe Lincoln answered, and bidding Ann and the preacher good-bye he went on his way.

John McNeil had come up just as Lincoln turned away. "Poor deluded sinner," Cartwright said kindly, looking after the tall, uncouth figure of Abe Lincoln. "How Satan does delude the soul of man, but he's worth praying for."

When John McNeil was alone with Ann Rutledge a few moments later, he said: "What did I tell you, Ann? I like Abe Lincoln all right, but I believe he is one of the worst sinners in this county. Why, even those Wolf Creek rowdies that tried to break up the meeting believe in hell."

"Folks don't see things the same way," Ann asserted thoughtfully.

"No—I suppose you'd call Abe Lincoln a saint."

Ann made no answer. She seemed just then to hear a bruised and helpless child saying: "God come, and His name's Abe Lincoln."

CHAPTER XIII

A Busy Sinner

While Peter Cartwright was laboring with every honest ounce of energy in his energetic soul and body to get his fellow men safely aboard the old ship of Zion, Abe Lincoln was finding diversions from the regular routine of store work, in kind as different as whipping a bully and feeding a baby.

The bully happened into the store one afternoon while Abe Lincoln was waiting on a couple of ladies. He had not seen the stranger before, and greeted him with his usual salutation, "Howdy, partner—come in."

It was soon evident that the stranger was on no friendly mission.

Hardly was he inside the store than he began to talk abusively and to deliver himself of an abundance of profanity.

Leaning over the counter Lincoln called the man's attention to the fact that there were ladies present. The man continued his abuse and swearing. Again Abe Lincoln spoke to him, this time saying in positive terms that no swearing was allowed when ladies were in the store.

The reply to this remark was worse swearing.

Abe Lincoln said nothing more until the ladies were gone.

Then he walked out from behind the counter and looked the stranger over.

"There's some sort of folks who can't listen to reason," he remarked. "Them kind has to have the daylights whaled out of them. What you need, partner, and what you are goin' to get is a spankin'."

This seemed to be what the stranger had desired. Pushing out his chest he stepped before Lincoln and told him to come on.

"Let's move out onto the face of the earth," Lincoln said. "I don't want to tear up the crockery and kick the molasses over."

When they were out at the side of the store and while the big bully was yet telling what he was going to do, he was seized suddenly, thrown to the ground and rolled over a couple of times. Then the tall man grabbed a handful of smartweeds and rubbed it in the eyes of the profane stranger until he bellowed like a bull.

A crowd had collected to discover what the row was about, among them John McNeil.

When Lincoln had extracted a promise from his visitor that he would keep his swearing for men only, he let him up and, taking him by the arm, led him back to the store steps and seated him. He then brought water, bathed the eyes of the subdued stranger, and shook hands with him.

This incident furnished talk for New Salem for a couple of days, and John McNeil made a special trip to camp meeting that night to tell Ann Rutledge about the fresh pugilistic outbreak of the tallest sinner in their midst.

In less than a fortnight after this incident, the stranger came again to the store with the request that Lincoln return with him at once to his home, as his wife was sick. He had recently moved out from Indiana and was not acquainted in the neighborhood, and he felt, some way, that Lincoln could help her.

To Honey Grove, a few miles distant, Lincoln went with him, and in a poor little cabin found a woman with a small baby. The woman was suffering from some sort of fever which had followed a severe chill.

"We didn't have nary remedy," she said with labored breath.

"Back at Wild Cat Run in Indianny, I had some black-dog ile rendered in the dark of the moon. Lots of folks was cured with it, but I couldn't git no black-dog ile, nor blood of a black cat, nor even the blood of a black hen here. Do you know whar thar's a black cat or dog? I'm powerful hot—I can't hardly breathe, I'm so hot. Jim, he says, if there's anybody in this neck of the woods can do it, it's Abe Linkum. Kin you help me? Do you know where there's a black dog?"

As the tall youth stood over the bed hearing the plea, his face was moved with pity.

"Yes, I'll help you. But I know something better than a black dog. We'll get Dr. Allen. He's the best doctor and got the biggest heart of any man in Illinois. He'll come and cure you."

Then Abe Lincoln wrote a few lines on a paper which he had in his pocket. "Hurry with bearer if possible, and bring Hannah Armstrong. We may save a mother's life. She has a little baby. A. Lincoln."

This he gave to the waiting husband, bidding him go back with all possible speed to New Salem.

At best it would be a couple of hours before the doctor could arrive, for it was several miles to town. Dr. Allen and Jack Armstrong both had good horses; Hannah was a fine rider, and Lincoln knew they would hasten if the doctor was not away on some other call.

When the husband had gone, Abe Lincoln found himself alone in a small clearing circled about by miles of woods. The short, heavy breathing of the woman broke the stillness of the warm fall afternoon. He turned to the bed and looked down at the sufferer. Her face was saffron-yellow, brightened to copper on her cheeks by flush of fever. Her eyes shone like glass. Her features were pinched, and her mouth drawn.

The young man by the bedside knew that unless help speedily came death was not far. Bending over her, he drew his long, strong fingers across her burning forehead.

"How good that feels!" she said, half closing her eyes. "You got fingers soft as a baby's."

He brought some water, and not being able to find a cloth, used his hand, making it cool and brushing her face very gently.

For a few moments she seemed easier, murmuring her thanks. "Your maw," she said, opening her eyes, "how she must love you."

"I have no mother," he said huskily, "not in this world."

"Your woman, then," she said, breathing the words out with labor, "every man has his woman."

He made no answer.

Under the touch of his cool hand she seemed for a time to grow quiet. But the fever was burning higher in her veins, and soon she began to rock her head and utter incoherent words.

Then she opened her eyes again. "I'm skeered," she said. "I'm awful skeered. I hain't done nobody no harm—but I ain't never been religious."

"Don't be afraid," he said huskily. "What is there to fear?"

"Hell—hell," she moaned, "I've heerd it preached."

Abe Lincoln started to say something reassuring, but again her mind was wandering. When she spoke now, it was of the baby lying on the back of the bed. After opening her eyes and steadying them, she half moaned, "He's hungry, the fever's dried me up—can you feed the baby? There's milk—there's milk——"

She did not finish the sentence. It seemed hard for her to speak.

"I'll find the milk and feed the baby. Don't worry," and he brushed her hot arms and hands and forehead with his big, wet hands.

Again she sank back into that restless drowsiness broken by moans and incoherent mutterings. Sometimes there was a sharp outcry, and always the labored breathing, growing ever faster and faster.

Abe Lincoln went to the door and looked anxiously up at the sun, and from the sun, down the roadway.

When he returned to the bed the woman wanted to speak again. She opened her eyes. At first there was only a glassy stare, but with an effort she gathered her vision and, fixing her eyes on the homely face by her side, she said with words that seemed beaten out by some raging inward force, "Abe Linkum, kin you pray?"

"Yes," he answered without hesitation, "what's prayer but callin' on God when there ain't no one else can help?—yes."

"Pray," she pleaded. "Kneel down and pray for me—I'm burnin' up."

The young man knelt beside the bed. The woman reached out and clutched him. He took her burning hand in his. By its pressure he knew that she was hearing what he said, as in a few simple words he brought to the attention of the Father the needs of a helpless and suffering child.

When he arose, the expression in the shining eyes told him the woman was still conscious.

A moment she looked into his face. Then she said: "'Tain't nothin' to be skeered of—is ther'? I ain't skeered no more—God, He won't let them git me and carry me to hell—God—God——" Then the intelligent light passed and the fitful fire of consuming fever took its place.

The end was at hand. Anxiously Abe Lincoln looked up the roadway, praying in his heart for a sight of Dr. Allen. The woman was raving wildly, and before another ten minutes had gone, life had left her body.

Abe Lincoln folded the hot hands over the fevered breast, straightened the head on the pillow and turned the cover up.

As he stood looking down on the clay tenement, the baby cried. After a brief search the milk was found, and taking the little one from its dead mother, the gawky young man began the task of feeding it with a spoon.

Scarcely had he finished this task when the ring of horses' hoofs sounded down the roadway. Good Dr. Allen was coming, and with Hannah Armstrong.

"Too late, Doc," Abe Lincoln said quietly, looking toward the bed. Then holding the baby to Hannah Armstrong, he said, "I've fed calves and pups, but this one seems to leak about the ears. So far all the milk has gone down its neck."

Hannah Armstrong took the baby. Dr. Allen was looking at

the hot body, which even now was beginning to turn black under the finger nails and about the mouth.

"Swamp poison," he said. "I could not have saved her—not today."

After Dr. Allen and Hannah Armstrong had gone back to New Salem, Abe Lincoln stayed long enough to help the woman's husband make a coffin.

On her way home, Hannah Armstrong stopped at Rutledge Inn to consult Mrs. Rutledge as to what should be done for the baby, and it was through her that Ann Rutledge heard a portion of the story.

"If there's any preacher or elder or deacon or shoutin' saint in this whole country that's doin' more for his fellers than Abe Lincoln, I want to see the color of his eye," declared Hannah. "He's fulfillin' the Scripture what says, 'Let not one hand know what the other one's doing,' and yet they say he's a sinner."

"I never heard Abe Lincoln called a sinner," Mrs. Rutledge protested in surprise.

"Yes, they do. Jack Armstrong himself heard John McNeil telling a bunch at Hill's store that Peter Cartwright himself said Abe Lincoln was a poor, deluded sinner." Then she turned to Ann and said: "Ann, if I was you, I'd speak to John McNeil about talkin' about Abe Lincoln. John McNeil's a nice fellow, best there is, but 'tain't fair for him to be pointin' Abe Lincoln out as a sinner. 'Twix the two of them, John with his ten thousand, and Abe Lincoln with nothin', I guess Abe's doing his share."

Ann gave Hannah Armstrong no answer.

The Spelling Match

During the fall season there were husking bees where merry
parties gathered to put away great piles of corn, partake of
bountiful dinners and play games in the evening. There were
also a number of log-rollings and new barn-raisings, at all of
which Abe Lincoln seemed to be a favorite. In fact, the ungainly
clerk in Offutt's store had come to be about the most popular
man in town among the men, boys and married women. He did
not, however, pay any special attention to the girls, and this
seemed out of the regular order, especially as they had a friendly
feeling for him.

With the coming of Christmas there was preparation for much
simple gift-giving. Ann Rutledge especially took this holiday
time for remembering more folks than any other girl in New
Salem.

One gift she had worked on with no small amount of pleasure was a gray yarn muffler for Abe Lincoln.

"He goes to all the debates and he might get a sore throat,"
Ann explained to her mother when asking her permission to
make the gift. "Besides, he hasn't any people and nobody else
might remember about him."

"You're a good girl to try to save Abe Lincoln's throat for the Debatin' Society," Mrs. Rutledge had said, laughing. "There'd be an awful long stretch of stiff neck if cold got into him."

Another of Ann's gifts was a fruit-cake bear made by her own hands for Ole Bar.

When she presented Abe Lincoln with his gift, it proved such a pleasant surprise that he was rendered speechless for the moment. At the same time she handed him the cake. "Give it to poor Ole Bar," she had said. "He seems to be all alone in the world, and I'm afraid nobody will think of him."

Ole Bar, as Abe Lincoln had been, was too much surprised to find words for adequate expression. The next day, however, he returned to the store and as soon as he got a chance to talk with the clerk alone he said, "Abry Linkhorn, me son Abry, every man what's a man and not a pipe-crower in breeches, mates. The Lord God made 'em that way, same as bars what brushes fur and courts in their own decent way. Fur reasons that no man hasn't been able to pick out of me, I haven't got me no Mollie and haven't no use for wimmin. But all them as isn't crippled nor fools nor too old to tote sticks, gets them one at some time. Now you git Ann Rutledge."

"But Ann Rutledge is goin' to be married next year to another man," Abe Lincoln said.

"Say, Abry, me son, did you ever hear of a bar standin' back like a holler-headed pip-jack when his Mollie was paradin' round in front of his eyes just because he thought some other bar was goin' to git her next year? If I must speak fer you, you never did. Nature comes fust. Just you git your own Mollie and let the other feller look out fer hisself."

"But she's promised, Ole Bar. She has given her honorable word."

Ole Bar chewed rapidly a moment. Then he stopped suddenly and said with decision, " 'Tain't nothin' to that. Wimmin is like bars. The best fighter gits the best female. If you show her what everybody else knows, that you're twice the man that deer-faced penny-grabber of hern is, she's yours, promise or no promise. Git

Ann Rutledge. 'Tain't nobody in forty years has thought of Ole Bar and sent him a present. She'll think of ye, Abry Linkhorn, *think* of ye. Ain't it worth fightin' fer to have somebody to *think* of ye? Ain't Ann Rutledge worth fightin' fer?"

Abraham admitted she was worth fighting for, and he thought of this the night of the big spelling match.

For the development of pioneer talent the New Salem Debating Society had been formed that winter, and had held some interesting meetings. There had been a number of men's meetings for the discussion of political subjects, which Abe Lincoln attended, but he had not yet appeared at the Debating Society.

The spelling match was to be preceded by a debate on the question, "Resolved that the Negro is more unjustly treated than the Indian?" Abe Lincoln had been invited to take one side, whichever he chose, and had said he didn't care which he took, he could win. So he was given the Negro side.

On the night of the important occasion the little school house was packed with men and women and children. Candles gleamed brightly on shingles which had been fastened into the chinks of the logs, and a big fire burned in the wide fireplace.

When Abe Lincoln arose to speak it seemed that his head would hit the rafters before he finally got straightened up. He wore jean pants five inches above his shoe tops, below which an expanse of blue yarn socks showed. His collarless shirt was fastened at the neck with a big white button. His coattail was so short that to sit on it would have been an impossibility, his heavy shock of black hair stood out sideways, and as he ran his hands down into his pantaloon pockets and stood for a moment as if embarrassed, a smile passed over the audience and they awaited eagerly the funny stories they thought he would tell, ready to burst into laughter.

After announcing his subject and beginning his speech, his hands came out of his pockets and his embarrassment disappeared. He forgot his surroundings in the earnestness of the thoughts he was giving expression to, and the men and women before him forgot they were not hearing a funny story and leaned forward listening earnestly.

"One man says to another," he said, "'you work, you toil, you earn the bread, and I will eat it.' But I say to you that whether it be a king with a crown on his head that says this, or whether it be a class with the power to force men, it all means slavery for the man whose toil, whose work, whose labor is not his own. . . . Peter Cartwright and others say the question of slavery or no slavery is spreadin', and that unless it is settled there will come war. . . . Why don't the Government buy the slaves and set them free? This would be right—this would be just—this might save human life and great expense which at last has to be paid by human labor." Then he told them about a slave-pen he had seen in New Orleans where men were sold as the farmers about New Salem sold hogs, and he gave utterance to that basic thought of Democracy that no man is great enough to control another man's freedom of thought or action.

Ann Rutledge sat with her father and mother. "There's something besides wit under that mop of black hair," Rutledge whispered as Abe Lincoln sat down. The homely orator was loudly cheered, Ann Rutledge with smiling face clapping heartily. Lincoln glanced her way, and as his eye rested on her for a moment he thought of Ole Bar's advice.

Then the spelling match was called. Sides were chosen and rows of young people from the age of Sis Rutledge to that of John McNeil formed one on each side of the room. Mentor Graham gave out the words from Webster's *Speller*, examples of their use being required as well as spelling.

Abe Lincoln and John McNeil were on the same side, Ann Rutledge stood opposite.

The schoolmaster opened the book toward the front, for an easy beginning.

"Nag," he gave out.

"N-a-g—My nag runs in the lot."

"Bib."

"B-i-b—Put on his new bib."

"Rude."

"R-u-d-e—A rude girl will romp in the street."

"Coach."

This word three sat down on. It was finally spelled.

"C-o-a-c-h—Few men can afford to keep a coach."

"Spark."

"S-p-a-r-k—What John McNeil does to Ann Rutledge when
Pa goes to bed."

A roar of laughter greeted this definition from Sis Rutledge
in which James Rutledge joined heartily. Dr. Allen, who sat op
posite Abe Lincoln, looked toward him. There was a smile on
his face, but it almost instantly passed, and gave place to an
expression the doctor did not have time to study, for the match
was going on.

"Pester."

"P-e-s-t-e-r—Never pester little boys."

"Foretop."

"F-o-u-r——"

"Next!" called the master.

"F-o-r-e-t-o-p—The hair over the forehead is called the fore
top."

"Pompions."

"P-o-m-p-i-o-n-s—Pompions are now commonly called pump
kins."

"Frounce."

"F-r-o-w——"

"Next!" called the master, and several sat down before it was
spelled.

"F-r-o-u-n-c-e—To frounce is to curl or frizzle the hair."

"Experience," the word was given to Abe Lincoln.

"E-x-p-e-r-i-e-n-c-e—Experience keeps a dear school, but fools
will learn in no other."

"Love"—the word was given to McNeil.

A giggle went around the room and the words, "John McNeil,"
were whispered as he spelled "L-o-v-e—love."

"Give the definition," the master said.

"Love is—is—love—is"—John McNeil hesitated and stopped.

"Who knows what love is?" Mentor Graham asked.

Half a dozen hands were raised, among them the big hand of Abe Lincoln, which seemed reaching into the rafters.

"Abe Lincoln," called the master.

"Love is an agreeable passion; love is sometimes stronger than death, and folks that love know it."

Mentor Graham dropped his eye on the open page of the spelling book. "Where did you get your definition?" he asked.

"From the book," Abe Lincoln replied.

"I mean the part that is not in the book?"

"I got that from—from——" and the big, homely youth hesitated, and then said, "that's just plain horse sense."

"Blasphemy" was the next word given out. It was John McNeil's turn to spell.

"B-l-a-s-p-h-e-m-y—A contemptuous treatment of God." McNeil spoke clearly and glanced toward Ann as if for approval.

After fifteen minutes of spelling, half the lines were seated. Ann Rutledge, John McNeil and Lincoln were standing. It was John's turn again.

"Relict."

"R-e-l-e——"

"Next!" said the master, and the word crossed the line to Ann.

"R-e-l——" she hesitated a moment and glanced toward Abe Lincoln who now stood opposite her. He had raised his hand to his face and one of his long fingers pointed to his eye.

"R-e-l-i-c-t——" she said slowly—"A relict is a woman whose husband is dead."

Again there was a titter and somebody whispered quite audibly, "John McNeil." But McNeil was not laughing. He had seen Abe Lincoln give a sign to Ann that had made her a better speller than himself.

Gradually the lines thinned until only eight remained. Then the master gave the word "Seraphim."

"S-e-r-y——"
"Next!"
"S-e-r-r-y——"
"Next!"
"S-a-r-a-h——"
"Next!"
"C-e-r-i——"
"Next!"
"C-e-r-y——"
"Next!"
"C-e-r-r-i——"
"Next!"
"S-e-r-r——"
"Next!"

It was now Lincoln's time. He had been waiting coolly. All eyes were upon him as he slowly spelled, "S-e-r-a-p-h-i-m."

"Correct!" said Mentor Graham. "Abraham Lincoln is the champion speller of New Salem until his better proves himself."

There was an outburst of applause. Lincoln started to take his seat, but the master motioned to him to keep his place. The room grew quiet.

"The definition, Abe Lincoln?" he said.

"The kind of folks we may associate with if we keep out of the Slough of Despond," answered Lincoln.

"Tell us where you got it," Mentor Graham said.

"I found it in Bunyan's *Pilgrim's Progress* one night as I lay before the fire, tryin' to learn something new. There was a wolf howlin' down in the timber. I tried to learn a new word between each howl. This was the third."

John McNeil walked home with Nance Cameron after the spelling match.

"Where is John McNeil?" Mrs. Rutledge asked as Ann joined them just outside the door, for he was always on hand to walk with her.

"He's walking home with Nance Cameron," Ann answered. "What's that for?"

"I guess he wants to tell her something," she said. But she too wondered, for he had not spoken to her, had not even seemed to see her, as he passed with Nance.

Others noticed this also, among them Dr. Allen and Abe Lincoln. But they made no comment as they walked down the roadway together.

CHAPTER XV

"Who's Afraid?"

It was Sis Rutledge who broke the news to Abe Lincoln that Ann said he was afraid of women. She went over to the store on an errand and tarried a few moments, as she always did when an excuse offered, to talk with the tall, good-natured clerk. This time Mrs. Green's quilting bee offered an excuse.

"Goin' to Mis' Green's quiltin' bee, are you?" Sis questioned with a sort of malicious innocence.

"Men don't go to quiltin' bees," Abe Lincoln answered.

"They walk as fur as the door," Sis said. "But you ain't like none of the rest of them. You don't spark none of the girls, nor take none of them to quiltin' bees nor sugar parties nor nothing. Ann says you're scared of petticoats."

"Ann Rutledge says I'm afraid of petticoats, eh? Tell Ann I'm comin' by this evenin' to see her."

With this astounding piece of news Sis hurried to Ann. She did not, however, report that part of the conversation which might have explained to Ann why he was coming.

"Is John McNeil going with you to Mrs. Green's quiltin' bee?" Abe asked when she came out to see what he wanted.

"No—John cannot go."

"Would he care if I walked over with you and the rest of hem?"

"I don't think he would. We'll all be going together."

"I'll be on hand then," and this was all Ann knew of the natter.

Mrs. Rutledge had gone over early that morning to assist Aunt Sallie Green—getting ready for such an important social unction as a quilting bee was no small matter.

First, there was the quilt to put in the frames and the thread and chalk and strings to have handy, and then there was the dinner, which took several days to prepare. The feature of most interest at the bee itself, however, was not the quilt or the feast, but the discussion of town topics, for women met at the bees who had not had an opportunity of discussing neighborhood news for weeks, and the time was never long enough to tell it all.

At Mrs. Green's one of the first topics for discussion was the postponed marriage of Ann Rutledge and John McNeil. "Ann promised to marry John McNeil and will sometime," Mrs. Rutledge said, "but her father wants her to have a good education, and he says there is no hurry in gettin' her off."

"I wouldn't take no chances in havin' an old maid in the family, if I was you, Mis' Rutledge," said Mrs. Benson. "I hate to give up my Phoebe Jane to Windy Batts, but I never would forgive myself if I stood in her way and caused her to be an old maid."

"Is Phoebe Jane going to marry Windy Batts?" was asked.

"Yes, I've consented. Windy's goin' out to convert the heathens of the West. He thinks he'll tackle the Indians and preach the Gospel and Phoebe Jane's goin' with him to sing."

"What did you Hard Shells turn Mentor Graham out of your company for?" Mrs. Rutledge asked. "He's the finest man in New Salem."

"It was his views on abstinence. Sunday schools, mission societies, temperance societies, nor none of such things is authorized in the Bible; you know they ain't, Mis' Rutledge. Well, if they're not authorized, they're a snare and delusion. Don't meddle with God's business, we say, and that's what a body does that talks against dram-drinkin' and tries to start a society."

"Dr. Allen says rum and such drinks is poison—real, sure enough poison," Aunt Sallie Green remarked.

This statement opened a lively discussion.

"Yes," said one, "and Dr. Allen couldn't get no sort of office after making a remark like that. Nobody can get anywhere without dram-drinking."

"Abe Lincoln don't drink anything stronger than cider."

"And he goes with the Clary Grove bunch, too. Wonder how he manages."

"No telling. The Creator broke up the mold after Abe Lincoln was made. He isn't like no human mortal I ever seen."

"Some folks says he's crazy," Mrs. Benson volunteered.

"It was lazy I heard he was," another said.

"I heard he was dead sure to go to the Legislature, crazy or no crazy."

"He's always reading something. Looks like he'd have all the books read through after a while. Wherever he walks he reads."

"Yes, and I've found him sprawled all over the cellar door reading," Aunt Sallie Green said.

"And did you ever see him lyin' under that tree in front of the store with his back to the ground and his long legs reaching up the tree? Phoebe Jane said he'd better watch or his legs would grow on up like bean vines."

"And somebody thought it was so funny, they went and told him," added Mrs. Cameron.

"Mercy!" ejaculated Mrs. Benson. "Was he mad?"

"No. He said he'd learned a new verse—something about seeing ourselves as others see us—he wasn't mad, though."

"And they do say he hasn't got but one shirt to his back—that he sends what little money he gets, off to his stepmother."

"And that he never looks at none of the girls. Is this true Mis' Cameron?"

"He don't seem to. The time we had that woman from Virginia and her two daughters, he slept at the store on the counter every night. But he's obliging that way when we're crowded."

"The men all say he's famous in stump speaking, wrestling and storytelling."

"And the women like him because he's honest, kind to women and forgetful of himself."

"He has a good turn for everybody and everything, from rabbits to such poor stuff as Snoutful Kelly. But he don't show no attention to girls."

"Maybe he has a girl at Gentryville or back on Pigeon Creek."

"I don't think so," Mrs. Cameron said, "and I'd be apt to know."

"Well, I don't know much about his affairs, only he never looks at Ann," Mrs. Rutledge observed. "He really don't pay as much heed to Ann as he does to Sis, and that's little enough. I don't suppose he knows what color her eyes are or her hair."

It was at this stage of the visit that the young people were heard coming across the fields, shouting and laughing.

Several of the women arose and looked out.

"Will you look!" Mrs. Benson exclaimed. "There's Abe Lincoln himself!"

"And he's with Ann Rutledge," Mrs. Armstrong observed.

"Abe Lincoln with Ann?" Mrs. Rutledge said, hurrying to the door.

For the moment she looked bewildered. Then she said, "He's wanting something—and just happened to walk with Ann."

"Just hear him laugh," said Aunt Green. "I'm glad he's come. He's a fine hand to take care of the baby."

At the door the other boys in the party declined to come in. Not so with Lincoln.

"Howdy, ladies, howdy—howdy!" he said, lifting his hat gallantly. "May I come in? I've heard tell of New Salem quiltin' bees and I'd like to see how it's done."

His welcome was as hearty as his self-invitation, and a few moments later he found himself tucked behind the quilting frame beside Ann Rutledge who was said to be the best quilter in New Salem.

Ann took out her needles, thread, thimble and emery bag. The end of a chalked string was tossed to her and she quickly made a few white lines.

"See the pattern, Abe?" Mrs. Cameron asked. "It's a tulip design, red flowers and green leaves. The blue is the pot it's growing in." In a few moments the company was quilting and conversation had again begun.

"We was just settin' in to talk about Peter Cartwright and the way he prayed the dancin' out of the legs in this community," Hannah Armstrong explained.

"I agree with him," Mrs. Benson said. "I'm down on all huggin', whether settin' or standin' still or movin' about. I haven't brought Phoebe Jane up the huggin' way. If I had, Windy Batts wouldn't have picked her to help him convert the Indians."

Abe Lincoln whispered something to Ann about a hugging match and laughed.

"I liked his singing," Mrs. Armstrong said. "I thought I'd cry my eyes out that night he sung 'Down the dark river where the dark willows are weeping night and day.' I never felt so near a graveyard in my born days. Everybody in the camp was mourning for some loved one."

"Wasn't that the same night he got around to eternal punishment and the thundering smell of smoke?" asked Mrs. Rutledge. "I heard it. After they got started they kept going until morning."

While the religious question was being discussed Abe Lincoln was watching the nimble fingers of Ann Rutledge as with one hand on the top side and one under the quilt she wove the tiny white stitches on the red and green and blue.

Presently the hand of Abe Lincoln disappeared under the quilt. The next minute a look of surprise showed on Ann's face as she whispered, "Turn loose of my hand."

"I'm just trying to learn how it's done," he whispered back.

Ann looked about. Nobody was paying any attention to them. She tried to move her hand but it was held as fast as if in a vise.

"I'll holler," she said.

"No, you won't," he whispered back.

Then Ann jerked her hand and for the moment it was free. She bent her slightly flushed face over the quilt and was soon making the white stitches again.

But Lincoln's hand was yet under the quilt, and before she had crossed the red tulip she felt her hand again imprisoned.

"Let go," she whispered, turning a flushed face to him and trying to work with one hand.

"I can't, I've got to hold on to somethin'. I'm afraid of women," was the answer.

The words were whispered in her ear. The flush on Ann's face deepened. She cast a glance around the quilt. Several were now looking at her and saw that she was confused. Her one free hand was working rapidly, but the stitches were being set crooked.

For a moment or two her hand was held in its prison. Once more he whispered, "Afraid of women am I, little Ann Rutledge?"

An instant she lifted her eyes to his. He had never known they were such beautiful violet blue. They were full of appeal, and Abe Lincoln could almost see tears coming.

He dropped her hand, and crawling out from behind the quilt, presented himself before Aunt Sallie and offered his services.

"I can wash dishes, carry wood, rock the baby, do anything that's needed," he said.

"A man like you ought to have a woman," Aunt Sallie Green observed.

"I'm afraid of women," he answered, laughing with boyish merriment.

Ann's face colored again slightly, but she joined the laugh with the others.

"Ready to go, Ann Rutledge?" he said when the party was over.

"I am waiting for Mother," she answered with quiet dignity.

He laughed. "Who's afraid?" he whispered as they started home. But Ann walked beside her mother.

This did not prevent word going out that Abe Lincoln was shining up to Ann Rutledge. What other reason on earth could there be for a young man attending a quilting bee and sitting by her and getting her all nervous right in the middle of her tulip-quilting.

CHAPTER XVI

Politics and Steamboats

There was considerable local pride in the pioneer hamlet of New Salem, and Abe Lincoln had entered into it with enthusiasm from the beginning of his citizenship. While he was ever present at political meetings and never silent, his opinion was that local needs were more pressing than national questions.

There were several needs which he continually urged. As good roads were at present out of the question, he advocated river traffic. With boats plying the Sangamon River, freight could be brought to their very door, and the farmer's produce, on the sale of which depended the future of the country, could be marketed at such a saving of time and money as would make the difference between failure and success.

So clearly did the young politician set forth this need that he soon had the majority of the men of the village of the same opinion. Another matter which he considered of first importance was the education of all children in free schools. This matter he also emphasized, showing in his crude but effective way that the future of Democracy depends on the education of the masses.

Having impressed his opinions on the men of the town their next question was how to get these laws. The logical answer was to elect to their lawmaking body a representative of these views.

Then it was that the uncouth young backwoodsman, without a dollar in the world and scarce a change of clothing to his back, was asked to represent Sangamon County in the next Legislature.

He agreed to do so, and issued a circular addressed to the "People of Sangamon County." In it he took up all the leading questions of the day: railroads, river navigation, internal improvements, and usury. He dwelled particularly on the matter of public education, alluding to it as the most important subject before the people. The closing paragraph was so constructed as to appeal to the chivalrous sentiments of Clary Grove. "I was born and have ever remained," he said, "in the most humble walks of life. I have no wealthy or popular relatives or friends to recommend me. My case is thrown exclusively upon the independent voters of the county; and if elected they will have conferred a favor upon me for which I shall be unremitting in my labors to compensate. But if," he concluded, "the people in their wisdom shall see fit to keep me in the background, I have been too familiar with disappointments to be very much chagrined."

A little after this the wonderful news was announced that a steamboat, already on the Sangamon River, was to pass New Salem. The captain had sent word that he wanted one of the representative men of the place to help him bring the boat to the village. Abe Lincoln was the man selected. A company of boys and young men also got together and with long-handled axes set out on horseback to go along the bank ahead of the boat and clear tree branches out of the way.

It was a time of great excitement and pregnant with meaning, for here already were signs that Lincoln's dream of river traffic might be brought to pass.

Hours before the appointed time the villagers were out, looking up at the sun to count the passing of time, or gazing down the river between the green branches. Speculation was rife, and there were those who boldly declared they never expected to lay eyes on a real steamboat, owing to their peculiar habit of blowing themselves up.

Almost to a minute of the announced time, as the sun stood, a shrill whistle sounded over the woods and fields and river— a strange sound for the quiet of the new country. Then came the distant shouts of the branch-cutters as they came riding down the banks swinging their long-handled axes.

Comment hushed to an occasional whisper as every head was turned and every eye strained to catch a first glimpse of the first steamboat that ever sailed the Sangamon.

Ann Rutledge was there. She was looking for a man as well as for a boat—a man she had first seen scarce a year before. The plums had been in blossom then. It was too early for them now. But she had her bonnet ready to wave.

As the boat came in sight a great cheer went up from New Salem on the bank. It was answered by the ringing voice of a man on board the steamer, a taller man than any of the others, who waved his hat and shouted across the water: "Hurrah for the Sangamon!" There were other messages, and then a loud, long cheer from the bank: "Hurrah for Abe Lincoln!"

The tree-cutters passed, singing and laughing. The boat steamed by like a bird. The people waved. As the boat neared the bank where Ann Rutledge and her mother and Mrs. Cameron and Nance stood, Abe Lincoln lifted his hat and held it clear of his head, and Ann waved her bonnet and laughed and sang a snatch of song.

As the boat passed from view the shrill whistle sounded several times. Ann listened.

"Nance," she said, "I like the horn better than the whistle. The horn has a gentleness, and it makes me think of plum blossoms. I would like to hear it again, just as it sounded a year ago. The whistle—it is hard—it sounds like blackberry briars."

Nance laughed. "But thorns go with blackberries," she said; "and travel must have its thorns, too, if it keeps up with what Abe Lincoln calls progress."

John McNeil joined the girls.

"Ann," he said, "you look very happy today."

"Yes," she replied, "I'm so glad about the steamboat."

"It's just about a year since Abe Lincoln first saw this town," he observed.

"Yes—it was April 19th, last year."

"You remember the date well."

"That was the day I found the first plum blossoms."

"And you found them just in time to wave at Abe Lincoln."

"I was glad he got his boat off the mill dam."

"Ann, what do you suppose Abe Lincoln came to New Salem for?"

"Maybe the same thing you did, John."

"I came to make money, and I'm making it. He didn't come to make money. He don't know how to make money and never will. Besides he gives away all he does get hold of."

"How do you know?"

"I found out. And who do you suppose he gives it to?"

"I don't know."

"His stepmother—stepmother!" and there was a strange tone in his voice whether of contempt or pity, Ann could not tell.

"Perhaps she is old and helpless," she said.

"Well, suppose she is, she's only his stepmother. If a man ever expects to get ahead he must save his pennies and let them make other pennies for him. That's the way to make money."

"I guess you know, John," Ann answered rather absently.

CHAPTER XVII

Captain Lincoln

James Rutledge and John McNeil were discussing Abe Lincoln as they sat around a low-burning fire on an early April evening. James Rutledge had just announced it as his opinion that Abe Lincoln had uncommon stuff in him and would make his mark in the world some way.

"I think Abe is a fine fellow," John answered, "but he'll never get anywhere."

"What makes you think that?"

"He doesn't know enough to get on the right side of a question. He's always taking up for something like nigger slaves. How's a man going to get anywhere in politics taking up with such notions?"

"I've never heard him say much about Negro slaves, one way or another," Rutledge said. "But the general principle of one man being held as property by another man, that's what Abe Lincoln gets after, and I think he's right."

"Do you know what he's taking up for now?" John McNeil asked.

"Haven't heard. What is it?"

"Indians, he's taking up for our enemies the Indians. A lot of the fellows were talking about the Indians. Ole Bar was telling the way they poison their arrows. He told some of the most blood-curdling cruelties you ever heard."

"And Abe Lincoln took up for the cruelties?"

"Not exactly that, but he said the Indians didn't do any worse than we would. They try to kill us and go at it the best way they know how. We try to kill them and, having bullets instead of arrows, kill more of them. Besides, he says this country belonged to them before it did to us, and we got it just as a big dog gets a bone away from a little dog. And he said more. He said that we, professing to be civilized and Christians, break our promises and treaties worse than they do."

Rutledge took his pipe from his mouth and slowly exhaled a thin cloud of smoke. Then he said: "Well, John, the only thing the matter with this is that it's all true."

"Maybe so," McNeil admitted. "But what's it going to get him, taking up for slaves and Indians."

"And poor little children whose fathers beat them, and women dying alone in the forest?"

It was Ann who asked this question. She had been sitting by her little sewing-table, mending stockings.

"That's what I'm asking," John McNeil repeated. "How's a man going to make money, fighting customers who swear in his store, or leaving his shop to hunt folks who have paid him a penny too much; or to get votes, taking up for folks that haven't any?"

The young man spoke quite seriously. James Rutledge laughed and then said: "It's the principle of things that counts. At present, however, only local issues are being discussed. On these Abe Lincoln is what we want."

"You'll lose your vote if you cast it for him. He'll never get anywhere politically. Mark what I tell you."

It was only a few days after this that the entire New Salem community was thrown into great excitement by news of an Indian invasion. Treaties had been broken and Black Hawk, the head of the warring Sacs, was again on the war path.

A company was immediately formed in New Salem to go out against the redskins. While the organization was yet forming, a demand was made for Abe Lincoln as captain.

He had a rival for the position and the choice was to be made by vote, each man as he voted to take his place behind the man of his choice. The voting progressed briskly. When it was finished the line headed by Abe Lincoln was three times as long as that of his rival. Great cheers were given, and Lincoln himself was exuberant with joy. A good horse was brought to him, the stirrups were lengthened, and he mounted. Some there were who had never seen him on a horse, perhaps. But now to the shouts of onlookers and members of his company, he showed himself a horseman of experience and the angular lines of his body took on a really military bearing.

With horses prancing and men shouting and calling, a parade was formed to march up the one street of New Salem. It was a motley crowd, some of them in buckskin, some in foxed and homespun breeches, with a generous sprinkling of coon-skin caps, that formed the company of Captain Lincoln. In addition to the Clary Grove gang, Wolf Creek patriots were there and the rowdies from Sand Town, and it was freely conceded by the cool-headed men of New Salem that not a man could handle such a crowd save Abe Lincoln.

Ann Rutledge looked on with smiling face and clapped her hands and shouted when Lincoln went prancing by on his good horse, his face bright with excitement and his black hair flying back from his forehead in the wind. But a shadow came over her face the night after the parade, and during the next few days, when every woman in town was foxing breeches for the company, she tried to see him, for she had something to say.

Unable to find an opportunity she sent Sis to tell him Ann had something to give him before he went away.

He came at once, and Mrs. Rutledge told him Ann was somewhere in the back yard.

He found her in the garden where a few peach trees were struggling into bloom.

"I've come, Ann," he said, stopping before her. "You sent for me, didn't you?"

"Yes, Abraham Lincoln. There's something I want to say to you before you go away. I've been holding it against you—but I want to tell you that I forgive you."

"Forgive me!" he said in astonishment. "What did I ever do to you that I should need forgiveness for?"

"Don't you remember the quilting bee?" she asked, her face flushing slightly.

"And you forgive me?"—he asked the question seriously. Then he laughed. "Don't forgive. Forgiveness might tempt me to do it again. Just remember as I go away that I'm not afraid of wolves or bears or catamounts or snakes or Indians, or any living creature—except women. It's women I'm afraid of," and he laughed.

The flush yet showed on Ann's face and her voice was a bit unsteady as she said, "And there's something else."

"What is it, Ann?"

"I—I don't want anything to harm you. I want you to come back sound and well."

There was pleading in her eye and a hint of quaver in her voice.

Abe Lincoln regarded her thoughtfully a moment. Her blue eyes did not shift before his steady gaze.

"Why do you want me to return unharmed?" he asked.

"Because you are kind to the weak and forgotten folks of earth, and not many think of this kind; because I think often what the child said."

"What child?"

"The beaten and abused child of old Kelly that you saved from more pain."

"What was it the child said?"

" 'God came,' " she said. " 'And his name was Abe Lincoln.' "

There was an almost imperceptible twitching in Abe Lincoln's face.

"There are many children," she continued, "many suffering,

sad and helpless ones who need a strong friend to help them.
My father says you have a future. I want you to come back to
your future."

"Do not fear for me. I will come back—to my future. Good-
bye." And he held out his hand.

"First, may I pin a sprig of wild plum on your coat for luck?
It's almost too early for them yet and I searched the thicket
before I found this, which looks as if it had only half opened
its white eyes, but it gives out its springtime fragrance to stir
up happy memories and hopes."

Abe Lincoln held out the lapel of his coat. "Look at me, Ann,"
he said when she had fastened the flower there.

She raised her eyes. They were rimmed with tears.

Abe Lincoln stared a minute as if wholly unable to compre-
hend the girl; then he said: "Good-bye, Ann, take care of yourself," and he turned hurriedly away.

CHAPTER XVIII

"Books Beat Guns, Sonny"

It was the tenth day of July when Abe Lincoln, who had for weeks been struggling through the swamps and forests of Michigan territory in pursuit of the fleeing Black Hawk, turned his face homeward.

The journey was made with many hardships. The remnant of the company went hungry for days, and to make matters worse several horses were stolen, among them Abe Lincoln's.

A portion of the long way home was made down the Illinois River in a canoe. The most of it, however, was tramped, and it was a jaded, footsore and ragged ex-captain that arrived in New Salem the latter part of July.

Nobody knew he was coming, no preparations had been made for him, and when he went to his former home at the Camerons' he learned that, owing to an increase in the size of the family, there was no longer bed space for him, but that James Rutledge had said he could lodge at the inn.

This was about the best news he could have heard, and tattered and weary, yet with head held high and smiling face, he presented himself at Rutledge Inn.

His welcome here was hearty and genuine, every member of

the family, even to Ann, trying to make him feel at home and all alike impatient to hear the story of his travels.

"Did you see the Indians scalp anybody?" Sonny asked excitedly.

"No—but we got there after half a dozen had just been scalped. We came upon them in the early mornin' just as the red sun fell over their bodies. There were small red marks on top of the heads. The men were scouts who had been surprised. One wore buckskin breeches."

"And did your men always give ready obedience?" asked Davy.

"Most of the time they did. Once I came near havin' a riot with them. An aged Indian bearin' a safe-conduct pass from General Cass came to camp. He was footsore, hungry and weary. The men did not want to receive him. They said he was a spy and should be killed, and they made plans to kill him. Just as they were about to proceed, their six-foot-four captain arrived and stopped proceedin's. This angered the men. One of them shouted at me that I was a coward. I told him to choose his weapon and step out and we'd see who was the coward. This he did not do. The frightened old Indian was sent on his way in safety."

"It was a hard campaign for you, and with little results," Rutledge remarked.

"Hard, yes—but not without results. There are different kinds of results, you know, Mr. Rutledge. I didn't kill any Indians, but I had far better luck than that. I got acquainted with Major John T. Stuart of Springfield, who asked to be of service to me."

"What's he going to do for you?" asked Davy. "Give you a fine gun or sword?"

"Better than that, Son, he is goin' to let me use his books."

"Books!" Sonny exclaimed, and the boy's voice was so charged with disgust they all laughed.

"Yes, books," Abe Lincoln replied. "Rattlesnakes and panthers and Indians know the fightin' game and have weapons for the purpose, but this sort of fightin' will never make the world a better place to live in. If the world ever gets to be the kind of a place you ask God for when you pray, 'Thy kingdom come,' it's comin' by brains and hearts instead of by claws and fangs. You can't shoot sense nor religion into a man any more than you can beat daylight into the cellar with a club. Take a candle in, and the thick darkness disappears; just so give the people knowledge and their ignorance and intolerance and other devilment will disappear. I haven't lived so powerful long yet, but I have lived long enough to make up my mind that for the good of all mankind books beat guns, Sonny."

CHAPTER XIX

Abe Makes a Speech

When Abe returned from his few months of service in the Black Hawk war, he learned that his political opponent, Peter Cartwright, had been making the most of his opportunity.

Abe Lincoln had announced his candidacy before he went away, but had had no time even to plan a speaking tour. Peter Cartwright had remained on his itinerary and had been speaking to large audiences. The weapon Cartwright had been using against his opponent with most telling effect was the implied charge that he was an infidel.

While Captain Lincoln had been gone from New Salem a minister had come to the hamlet to make his home, and was already one of the circle composed of Mentor Graham, Dr. Allen, William Green, James Rutledge, and other of Abe Lincoln's good friends.

Even before his return these friends had discussed the matter of religion as it pertained to the success of this candidate, and had decided, especially since Cartwright was making much capital out of the fact that Abe Lincoln was not a church member, that he should become one.

Accordingly he was called into council and the case set before him.

"It is not necessary that I go to the Legislature to keep my own self-respect," he said to them. "It is necessary, however, that I deal honestly with myself, and it would be neither fair to me nor to your society for me to become a member, since I do not believe as you claim to. I have no use whatever for a God that plots against innocent children and helpless women, encourages murder, that throws rocks down on honest soldiers and, as recorded, does many other foolish and wicked things which would shame a decent Indian. I'm familiar with the Good Book—too familiar to swallow some portions of it whole. Whenever you get together on the rule 'Love your neighbor' that Jesus himself taught, I'll join you."

"Cartwright is making much of your refusal to be counted with Christians."

"And by doin' just this thing Cartwright is provin' himself either ignorant of the Constitution of the United States or knowingly betraying it. Our Constitution stands forever for the separation of Church and State, of religion and politics. If my common, everyday horse sense will not let me believe in purgatorial fires, what has that to do with making Sangamon River navigable? If I haven't any better sense than to pray to an image, that's my affair so long as it is not allowed to enter into or affect my public policies, or I do not try to inflict it on someone else. This is what I make out of our Constitutional guarantee of civil and religious liberty. I haven't had much chance to go to school. I haven't had many books to study. But, gentlemen, I've eaten up the Constitution of our country and digested it a dozen times over. I may get its meaning wrong. I think I'm right. If I am, then Cartwright is wrong—just as wrong as I would be to campaign against him because he preaches hell fire and eternal punishment, which to me is as damnable a doctrine as my lack of such belief can ever be to him."

"Abe Lincoln," said James Rutledge, "I believe you are right. Stand by your guns. You may lose now but you will come out all right in the long run."

Abe Lincoln's first appearance on the stump in this campaign was at Pappsville, a small place eleven miles west of Springfield. A public sale had been advertised and the young candidate thought it would be a good chance to get a hearing.

After the sale a friend who had accompanied him went about shouting, "Public speaking! Draw near! Draw near!"

The crowd soon collected, for every man was interested in a stump speech.

Hardly had the crowd gathered than a fight started and a general row seemed inevitable.

Seeing a friend of his being pushed about by the rough crowd, Abe Lincoln jumped from the platform, and rushing into the crowd, began shouldering the excited men apart so that his man could get out. Finally, he pushed against a man who turned about and defied him. Without a word he grabbed the man by the neck and the seat of the breeches and tossed him a dozen feet. This act had a quieting effect on the fight and the fighters stopped to see what manner of political candidate this was who could pitch men about as a farmer pitches a shock of wheat.

What they saw on the rude platform was an unusually tall, ungainly and homely young fellow, who wore a mixed-jeans coat, bob-tailed and short-sleeved, pantaloons made of flax and tow linen, a straw hat and pot-metal boots.

His speech was short. He said, "Gentlemen and fellow citizens, I presume you all know me. I am humble Abraham Lincoln. I have been solicited by my friends to become a candidate for the Legislature. My politics are short and sweet like the old woman's dance. I am in favor of a national bank. I am in favor of the internal revenue system, education for everybody, and a high, protective tariff. These are my sentiments and political principles. If elected I shall feel thankful. If not, I am used to defeat. It will be all the same."

CHAPTER XX

Story of a Boy

Abraham Lincoln was not elected to the Legislature. He received, however, every vote in New Salem except three, and his friends had hopes that he might yet develop into something—nobody knew just what.

Meantime some changes had been made in mercantile affairs in New Salem and the store of Offutt was no more. This left Abe Lincoln without a job.

An opportunity offered for him to secure a store of his own. A store owned by another man had not long since been raided by the Clary Grove gang. After drinking all the "wet goods," they broke the glassware, tied bottles to the tails of their horses, and with a whoop and a yell went riding about the country.

Abe Lincoln had no money, but with a young fellow named Berry, whose father was a leading Presbyterian citizen, he bought the store and they gave their notes in payment.

Certain it was the Clary Grove gang would not molest Lincoln's store. On the other hand, they would fight to protect it.

In fitting up this store Lincoln and Berry took out a tavern license, which gave them the right to sell liquor in small quantities. All stores kept liquor. Yet this fact did not make it seem right that one who did not drink himself, who knew the trouble it made others, who even agreed with Dr. Allen that it was poison, should keep a barrel of whiskey in the corner of his store, and more than one discussion between Abe Lincoln and the good doctor were engaged in during these days.

Several treasures came into possession of the junior member of the firm after Berry and Lincoln opened their store. Lincoln one day bought a barrel. What it contained he did not look to see. It was a good barrel. The man said it had a book or two down under the papers, and as he needed the few cents badly, the purchase price was paid and the barrel put aside.

When some weeks later the contents were poured out, Abe Lincoln discovered a treasure. He deserted his store long enough to run over to Rutledge's to make known his wonderful good luck. His homely face was bright with pleasure and his dull, gray eyes were shining as he held out a worn and stained copy of Blackstone.

"Look! Look!" he cried, and in his joy he even tried to dance a jig.

Another rich possession that came to him was a volume of poems containing one that he especially liked and the title of which was "Immortality."

This poem Abe Lincoln wanted to read the Rutledges as they sat around the fire on an early fall evening.

But Davy did not like the sound of the first verse and asked for a story of the killing of Abe Lincoln's grandfather by Indians. When this was told he wanted to hear about the voodoo fortune-teller in New Orleans and the slave markets and the ships in the harbor.

So Lincoln told these things while James Rutledge smoked and Mrs. Rutledge and Ann busied their fingers with their mending, meantime listening with as much interest as the children to their boarder's talk.

After Davy's stories had been told it was Sonny's turn. "Tell about when you were a little boy," he urged; "that's what I want."

Nothing could have been more acceptable to the entire family than this, for he had never said much about his own affairs.

"The little boy you ask me to tell about," he said, "lived far away in a dense forest; wild cats screamed down the ravines; wolves howled across the clearin'; bears growled in the underbrush. The house this little boy lived in was not much better than the cave or the den of the animals. It was built of logs but had no floor, no windows, and no skin hung to the door. In a loft above the one room was a nest of leaves and into this he climbed at night on pegs driven into the wall.

"Though he was very poor, this little boy was rich in one thing, and that was his mother. She toiled until her shoulders were stooped and thin, her face pale and her clear gray eyes dim and sad, but she was never too tired to love her children, the boy and his little sister Sarah. She could read well and had brought into the wilderness three books: the Bible which she read daily, *Pilgrim's Progress,* and Aesop's *Fables.* Before the boy learned to read she told him stories from these books in the yellow light of a pine torch which burned upon the hearth, and the boy minded not the cry of wolves, nor wind, nor sleet, when he could hear these wonderful stories.

"The boy was taught many things that boys on the frontier must know. He learned early to skin animals and fix the hides for clothes but he was never a hunter. He some way felt that the animals had a right to life, just as he had. They knew what it was to be hungry and cold and to sleep in leaves. It was a funny notion, but the boy felt in a way they were his brothers and he never killed them.

"After he learned to read he spent hours on the floor lyin' in the firelight with the Bible spread before him, spellin' out the words and learnin' the verses until he had read the Book many times.

"When he was nine years old his mother made him a linsey-woolsey shirt and possum-skin cap to wear with his buckskin breeches and sent him away through the woods to school. He only went for a few weeks. The boys in this school put coals on terrapins' backs. He was not quick to learn from his books but he made speeches against this cruelty, and his first fight was with a boy for robbin' a bird's nest.

"In one school he went to for a short time later, a master named Crawford taught manners. He made one boy stand at the door. When the pupils came up they were taught to lift their hats and were introduced to each other. This teacher said manners were as important as book knowledge.

"The boy only went to school a few weeks altogether, when he was hired out by his father to work from sunrise to sunset for twenty-five cents a day. Still he studied, and a cousin named Dennis Hanks helped him. They made ink with blackberry root and copperas. They made pens of turkey-buzzard feathers. When they had no paper, which was most of the time, they wrote on boards with charred sticks. The boy figured on a wooden shovel and scraped it off clean when it was too full to hold more figures.

"His mother was always interested in his effort to get an education. She always helped him. She was sorry for him because he could not go to school, but urged him to learn so that he would not always be in the backwoods.

"Once he borrowed from the Crawford man who taught the school a book entitled *Weems' Life of Washington*. It told about our country's struggle for freedom, how the Hessians were fought and how Washington crossed the Delaware. He pored over it until the night. He took it up into a loft and put it in a chink so it would be handy for early-morning study. A rainstorm which arose in the night beat in on the book and swelled the covers. The boy took the book back to its owner the next mornin' and offered to buy it. The man made him pull fodder three days for it. The book belonged to the boy now. He read it over and over until he became well acquainted with the Father of his Country and began to dream dreams of what he might some day do."

Abe Lincoln had been talking in a reminiscent mood with a half-smile on his face. The smile now passed. He continued: "Then death came into the settlement and took several neighbors. The mother of the boy was stricken down. She was thirty-five miles from a doctor and her nearest neighbor was dead. Seven days she lay, her children doin' for her. Then she called the children to her bedside. To the boy she said, 'Be an honest and a faithful boy, be a good and tender man. Look after your sister.' Then death came into the shack of a house and took the patient mother.

"The boy's father built a coffin and dug a grave in the clearin' near the house, and here in the edge of the dense forest where the wild things lived the tired mother's body was put to rest. There was no preacher to say a last word, there was no music but the singin' and the sighin' of the trees. There was no one to cover the rude coffin with earth but the father. There were no mourners but the two children, holdin' hands beside the grave and callin' their mother to come back.

"After the mother had gone the little girl tried to cook and keep house. The boy went every day to the edge of the forest. Very soon the tangle began to reach over his mother's grave. He wanted her to have a funeral sermon. It was not that he thought she needed it. He was sure she was with God all straightened up and no longer thin but always smilin' and glad. But she would have wanted a sermon, she had spoken of it.

"So, the boy wrote a letter to a good Baptist minister his mother had known back in Kentucky and told him what was wanted. It was nearly one year later that he came a distance of eighty miles to preach the sermon. All the people in the country came; not before had a funeral been preached when a woman had so long been sleepin' in her grave. And, as they gathered about, their faces were wet with tears. The boy never forgot it, nor the preacher's words.

"That little boy is a man now. Early one mornin' years ago he went for a last time to the lonely grave and kneelin' there, promised his mother's God again that he would be honest and tender. And whatever that boy is now or ever may be, he will owe to that angel mother lyin' under the wild tangle at the edge of the forest with God's stars watchin' it until the Judgment Day."

It was quite still around the low-burning fire when he ended his story. Then James Rutledge spoke abruptly, "Davy, don't you see the fire needs a log? Sonny, put Tige out, he's scratching down the house. Ann, bring a pitcher of cider and a plate of apples."

"Put a few sweet turnips in," Abe Lincoln added; "there's nothing better than a turnip."

CHAPTER XXI

Only Wasting Time

After Abe Lincoln went to Rutledges' to board, time seemed to go faster and more pleasantly than ever in his life for him. James Rutledge was not only an agreeable gentleman, but he was an unusually well-informed man for a pioneer, and he and the little coterie of friends passed many winter evenings discussing topics of local and national interest.

Abe Lincoln spent very little time, however, at the Rutledge home. There were many debates and public meetings during the winter, all of which he attended. His treasured Blackstone was being read and digested with the same thoroughness he had given Washington and the Constitution and the Bible. In addition to this he had secured, at no small outlay of time and expense, a grammar, said to be the only one in the county, which he was eagerly learning. He was also making the acquaintance of Shakespeare, with which he was immoderately delighted, and which he had announced he would learn by heart as he had much of the text in the few books he possessed.

Besides his newly acquired Blackstone and Shakespeare, Lincoln was making trips to Springfield to borrow from Major Stuart what seemed to the country youth an inexhaustible wealth of books.

So it happened that nights when there was no meeting of

any kind, Abe Lincoln studied alone in the store or sometimes at the cooper shop, where warmth and light were given him.

The winter of the busy year came early to New Salem, and the hamlet was wrapped in a sheet of white which covered the roadways and fields, and draped the bluffs, and bent the boughs of the forest trees. The streams were muffled and, save where dark spots showed water moving sluggishly, were hidden under the white blanket. Cattle huddled by the haystacks and in barns, and in the log houses great fires blazed on the hearths and the store of candles was drawn on heavily to make light for the long evenings when the housewives used the time to spin and knit.

It was a bitter-cold night that Abe Lincoln after supper sat a few minutes by the fire. James Rutledge had gone to Springfield and would not return until next day. There was no meeting, and Mrs. Rutledge and Ann thought perhaps their boarder would spend the evening with them.

The wind blew low and seemed to hug close to the earth and move silently and stealthily as if trying to envelop some victim unaware. The snow crunched at the slightest tread. The hearth fire had never seemed so good.

Abe Lincoln and Ann were alone in the room. He sat before the fire looking at the coals; she was getting her spinning ready.

Rising suddenly he took his hat and gray muffler from the peg on the wall.

"You're not going out, Abraham?" Ann inquired.

"Yes—I'm going over to Muddy Point."

"To Muddy Point?" Ann exclaimed setting her wheel down.

"Yes. I have it as straight as the crow flies that Snoutful Kelly's wife and children are actually sufferin' for food. Do you suppose your mother will fix up a basket?"

"Of course—but, Abraham—this is the coldest night of the winter! Mother!" Ann called rather excitedly, "come here!"

Mrs. Rutledge entered with a yellow bowl in which she was beating buckwheat batter to put by the fire to rise for breakfast cakes.

"Mother!" exclaimed Ann. "Abraham says he is going to Muddy Point."

Mrs. Rutledge turned and stared at Abe Lincoln a moment as if to make sure he were there. Then she said, "Are you joking, Abraham?"

"No, indeed—I'm goin'. Old Kelly's wife is sick and the children are hungry. I got it straight, and I can't sit by this warm fire so comfortable and think of them sufferin'. I've got to go."

"But, Abraham Lincoln, there is not another person in New Salem, not a living soul of them, that would do it such a night as this."

Abe Lincoln laughed. Then he said, "That's all the more reason I must go. Will you send a basket?"

"To be sure—but it's an awful cold night and you haven't any long coat."

"I'll walk fast enough to keep warm," he assured her. "If folks waited until all signs were right for doin' these little things, they'd never get done. We only pass this way but once, you know. Any good thing we can do we must do as we go—we don't come back."

Mrs. Rutledge stood looking at the tall, ungainly youth. For a moment his face seemed to be beautiful as the firelight fell on its strong lines. Then without a word she returned to the kitchen. In a moment she called Ann to come and help her. Abe went out, too, and together they fixed a basket and covered it well so that it would not be frozen when delivered.

Abe Lincoln was not warmly clad for cold weather. Ann thought of this as he stood before the fire holding his big square muffler.

"This will keep me warm," he said, wrapping it about his throat.

"You haven't any gun," Ann said. "Wolves killed three of William Green's pigs yesterday, and last week there was a great big catamount at Honey Grove."

"Do you remember what I did to Armstrong? I did a catamount that same way once. I always carry my weapons. God fastened them to me so tight I can't leave them."

Ann and her mother laughed. Abe Lincoln went out into the cold, and they heard the sharp crunching of the snow under his quick footsteps.

"I'm going to spin tonight, Mother," Ann said. "You don't care if I put the kettle on and make Abraham something hot to drink when he comes home, do you?"

"A very good idea," Mrs. Rutledge said. After she had done some mending she put the water pail by the fire, hung a roll of pork sausage on the wall, and after having taken other precautions to insure a good warm breakfast when everything would be frozen up the next morning, she went to bed, and Ann was left to spin and to think.

Never was Ann Rutledge long alone that she was not singing. So now, as her wheel turned in the firelight, she began to sing a glad song full of life and hope and joy crowded into the words and melody of the old tune, "O, how I love Jesus!"

As the fire, eating its way through the back log, told the passage of time she stopped and listened. The kettle was steaming and on the kitchen table was a plate of food waiting to be brought in.

At last the crunching of the snow under heavy footfalls told her he was coming. But she only turned her wheel a little faster and sung a little heartier as he entered, lest he should know she had been watching.

"O, how I love Jesus!" Abe Lincoln hummed as he came by the fire and rubbed his hands. "Go on with your song and your work. While I get warm I will tell you a story.

"Once there was a great camp meetin'," he began, settling himself in James Rutledge's big splint-bottom chair. "There was an exhorter named Barcus who helped stir things up to the boilin'-over point. Among those who got shoutin' happy was a fair and fond sister. Brother Barcus and the sister both danced and shouted toward each other. When they met, he said, his benign countenance shinin' with joy, 'Sister, do you love Jesus?' 'Oh, yes,' she whispered rapturously, 'yes—yes—yes.'

" 'Then kiss brother Barcus,' was this shepherd's advice to his beloved sheep."

Abe Lincoln settled back. Ann laughed. Then she said, "Abraham, we are bad—you for telling such a story and I for listening."

"No, we are good," he corrected, "you for not askin' the woman's name and I for not tellin' whether she kissed Brother Barcus."

Again Ann laughed. Then she glanced at Abe Lincoln and from him to the peg where his hat hung.

"Where is your muffler?" she asked. "You didn't lose it, did you?"

The tall man looked into the fire a moment before saying, "No—I gave it away."

"Gave it away?"—and there was a tone of disappointment in her voice.

"Yes. I'll tell you about it. When I got out to Kelly's I found the poor woman in bed, and a newborn baby. The little thing didn't have any clothes or any warm blanket to wrap around it. I looked at that fine, thick, warm, wool muffler all made by your hands, and I hated to give it up. But that baby, Ann—it was such a little helpless thing and so pitiful, and its mother's eyes looked in such a hungry way at that gray muffler, I couldn't help it. So I wrapped it up myself. And I felt that if you had been there you would have done the wrappin'. In fact, I could see you foldin' the warm cover around that poor little thing. You would have done it—wouldn't you, Ann?"

"Yes, Abraham."

"I was sure of it. Perhaps you'll make me another some time. Now go on with your spinnin' and your song. It is the best music a tired man could ever hear."

Ann turned the wheel a few times, but she did not sing. "When a woman gets loving Jesus," he observed, "it's a sign she's lovin' somebody else. Who do you love, Ann?"

This unexpected question took Ann quite by surprise.

"You know as well as I do that I am engaged to marry John McNeil. And don't you think he is one of the best young men in town?" There was a suggestion of appeal in the question.

"I am sure he is—one of the very best in the county. But tell me, Ann, what it is to love. You know the spellin'-book definition. It's in the Bible, too, that love is stronger than death. But they both came out of somebody's mind first, somebody who loved. Tell me about it."

"Why should I know?"

He mused a moment, then he said as if to the fire instead of Ann: "It won't be until I *know* that I promise to marry a woman."

Ann glanced at Lincoln. He seemed for the moment unconscious of her existence. She called him from his reflections by speaking his name.

"Abraham," she said as the wheel spun slowly, "I have a secret to tell you, a confession to make."

He was all attention in a minute. She dropped her hands in her lap and moved a little way from behind the wheel.

"Do you remember the camp meeting, and Brother Cartwright saying you were a deluded sinner, and saying you were worth praying for?"

"Did he? I believe he did."

"Well, since that night, every day I have been remembering you at the throne of grace, but I have made up my mind it is only wasting time. I still don't understand how anybody can be saved and not believe in hell, and you do some things that are not right, like the day at the quilting bee, which was not fair to John McNeil. My Bible says, 'By their fruits shall men be known,' and, Abraham, your life bears fruit, much better fruit and more of it than do some of those who call you a sinner. So I've decided it's just wasting my time and God's to pray for you any more."

In the moment of silence that followed this speech, Ann turned back to the wheel.

"Don't spin," he said; "there's something I want to say."

She folded her hands in her lap and waited. There was no sound in the room save the sputter of the fire. A bit of charred wood fell into the ashes. Lincoln took the tongs and threw it back, then he sat looking at it.

Presently he turned to Ann. "And you have been rememberin' me at the Throne of Grace? I don't know anything about thrones and mighty little about grace, for the grace of life has not been my portion. But this is what I want to say. If a man can get to God through the intercession of a true and noble and pure-hearted man, as all Christians say they do, I don't see why a man can't get to God through the pleadin's of a true and noble and pure-hearted woman."

Ann looked at him questioningly.

"I don't know what you mean, Abraham," she said.

"I mean just this—if ever I reach the throne of grace where just men get nearer glimpses of God, it will be through—Ann Rutledge. Do you understand this?"

Ann's eyes had not for an instant left the figure of the man who was speaking. The homely, bronzed face in the frame of black hair, the slightly stooping shoulders, the big hands stretched at full length on the arms of the chair, made a fire light picture fascinating to the girl. He had asked a question—she had not answered it, yet she leaned forward, and after studying his face a moment she said, "Abraham, you look as if you were starving. I must get you something to eat"; and she hurried to the kitchen.

Lincoln leaned forward and buried his face in his hands. "It wouldn't be fair to John McNeil," he seemed to hear her saying again, and with a deep sigh he said in his heart: "Separated by the rules of the game of honor."

"Ann," said Mrs. Rutledge the next morning, "what did you and Abe Lincoln find to talk about so long last night?"

"Camp meetings and mufflers and Kelly's new baby," Ann answered.

"You must be careful, Ann," her mother said. "Your word is

out to John McNeil and he has a good start in life. Abe is a fine boy and honest as the day is long, but he hasn't got anything to take care of a woman on. Besides, he does all sorts of queer things. For all we know he may yet take to writing poetry. You must not give him any encouragement. Since that quilting bee I've had some thoughts. He wasn't there to learn to quilt. He'd be fearful hard to get shut of if he got in love good and hard."

"He has no idea of love at all," Ann hastened to assure her mother. "He doesn't even know what it means. He told me so."

"That's the worst kind to get stirred up. The kind that just naturally knows how, are always having attacks of love the same as they do attacks of measles. But the kind that has to be waked up and taught by some woman have terrible bad cases. Don't you get Abe Lincoln stirred up."

"He doesn't care for girls, anyway—no particular ones. He likes books and is not the kind to fall in love."

"Love can pipe through any kind of a reed," was Mrs. Rutledge's answer. "Don't stir Abe Lincoln up."

CHAPTER XXII

Town Topics

Not many months had elapsed after Abraham Lincoln went into the "store business" before those interested began to feel that John McNeil had not been mistaken when he said Lincoln would not be a success as a business man.

After everybody else in town was questioning whether or not the store was making money, Lincoln himself declared it was petering out.

This in no way interfered with his storytelling and studying hours. The store was headquarters for political and all other kinds of discussions, and study hall for the most unwearying scholar in the village.

So it happened that when Abraham should have been devising schemes to make money he was memorizing Blackstone, debating some point of Constitutional law, or working out some rule of grammar.

Nor was this the worst. While Lincoln was letting the store go to ruin for lack of business skill and application, his partner, Berry, was drinking up the wet portion of the stock.

John McNeil looked on with disgust and made comments,

many of them to Ann Rutledge. She could not deny them, for she had found Abe Lincoln a most absent-minded and in some ways a most unsatisfactory boarder.

More than once she had rung the bell at mealtime with no success at bringing Abe Lincoln to the table. Once when she was sure he must be half-starved she went to the store to bring him. She found him stretched on the counter with head propped up against a roll of calico, deeply buried in a dingy, leather-bound book. When she finally drew attention to herself from the book he said: "Run back home, Ann, Blackstone is making a point. I'll be there in a few minutes."

Determined that he should eat, after waiting an hour she went back to the store carrying a plate of food. "Abraham Lincoln," she said, "you've got to eat."

"What for?" he asked absently.

"Because if you don't you'll get to be nothing more than a human grapevine and you won't even be as good-looking as you are now."

"What's that?" he said, looking up after finishing the sentence he was reading. "Say that again."

She repeated her remark. Lincoln laughed. Then he said, "Put the feed on the molasses barrel. I'll get it in a minute," and he turned back to the book.

When the Lincoln and Berry mercantile company had so far gone to the bad that the end was in sight, the nominal owners sold out to a couple of men who paid them, as they had paid, with notes.

Free from the store, Lincoln was now ready for another occupation, and at this time was appointed postmaster, a very small job since the mail came but twice a week in good weather, with pay accordingly.

It gave him time for study, however, which he continued on his rounds of delivery, for with the three or four letters that might come in a week, placed carefully in the top of his hat, he would start out to deliver them. Between stops he would mount a fence where the rails crossed under the shade of some tree, and here he would read and reflect and memorize, oblivious of time or men or finances.

There was always plenty to talk about in New Salem, and for that matter plenty to do the talking. The last baby's first tooth had a significance, for by the baby's age might be forecast the time of the next one's arrival. The last tooth of the oldest citizen was likewise of importance, as it called out all the best recipes for mush and other nourishing soft edibles.

Among the more important news was the announcement, after he had served some months as postmaster, that to this official duty Abe Lincoln was to add the most important one of surveyor. He had already received the appointment and was taking lessons in figures from Mentor Graham, preparatory to starting out with his rod and chain.

It seemed to make no difference in Abe Lincoln's popularity that he had failed as a business man. He was still considered the best man in town, the best judge or referee, an authority in disputes and a peacemaker. He was the best-informed man on general subjects and the gentlest as well as the strongest man among them.

His wider acquaintance throughout the county served to enlarge the number of his friends, and New Salem politicians again decided to make him their candidate for the Legislature.

In addition to his new professional work, Abe Lincoln had entered the ranks of the reformer in a manner as strenuous as it was unique.

Having become exasperated with the drunkenness of Snoutful Kelly and the consequent neglect of his family, Abe Lincoln and a sufficient corps of assistants determined to get some sense into his head by a new way. Accordingly, they captured Kelly while lying by the roadside in a drunken sleep, and removing him quietly to the top of the long, sloping street at New Salem, proceeded to fasten him up, in an empty whiskey barrel, which they started on its way down hill.

Long before the barrel reached the bottom of the road it gave forth such sounds as never disgraced a music box, and the men waiting at the foot of the hill roared with laughter as the barrel went its way down, emitting howl after howl, and yell after yell, as it bumped its course to the bottom.

When it had reached its stopping point, Lincoln stood it on its end and through the bung hole called Kelly's attention to the ducking he had once got with such salutary effect and made him swear by the God above him, and those present, that he would never touch another drop, lest a more horrible fate should befall him.

When the victim of reform crawled out he was brushed off by Lincoln and given a handful of change, with instructions to proceed back where he got his whiskey, which he had relieved himself of in the barrel, and buy some meat and flour to take home.

This reform experiment had not been advertised. But it was town talk the next day. The men generally said it was a good thing for old Kelly. Some of the women disagreed. Ann Rutledge said the man who had sold whiskey had no business punishing the man who drank it.

After this came a few days of another kind of discussion of Abe Lincoln. It was rumored that he was studying to be a lawyer. Opinion was divided as to whether this would make a man of him or ruin him.

Mentor Graham and Dr. Allen were agreed that he already knew the Constitution as well as any lawyer in Springfield and would make a good lawyer. To others it seemed a pity that an otherwise honest citizen should aspire to nothing better than being a "limb of the law," and when Ole Bar heard it he said with a touch of real sadness, "Lord God, has Abry Linkhorn fallen to this? I'd ruther he'd a been a bar."

Whatever might be the outcome, New Salem never worried long over any one matter. There was too much coming on afresh.

The next topic, and one that especially interested the female portion of the community, was the discovery that John McNeil's partner was also in love with Ann Rutledge.

This leaked out in an unexpected way.

Abe Lincoln being everybody's friend and knowing how to read and write, was often called on to write letters for less educated lovers, for children and sometimes for business men. He also read for those who could not read. This was expected of him as postmaster. One day a schoolchild brought a roll of written matter to him. It was composed of bills from the Hill and McNeil store. But inside was a letter from Hill to McNeil charging that if McNeil had played fair, his partner, too, might have had some chance to win the fair Ann Rutledge.

When Abraham Lincoln read this letter he was for some reason well pleased, and he understood why Hill was always so exceptionally nice to Ann Rutledge and gave her better bargains than his close and businesslike partner would have thought of doing.

Yet he felt sure that Ann did not know of his burning affection or she would not so often have gone to the store or accepted so many favors of him.

After some consideration his sense of humor got the best of him and he decided to take the papers to McNeil himself. This he did. When asked if he had read the letter, he admitted without hesitation that he had, and offered a friendly bit of jollification.

Immediately there were words between Hill and McNeil. Lincoln tried to act as pacifier and the letter was put in the stove. Several bystanders had heard the difficulty, however, and were not slow to get its meaning. Hill was in love with Ann Rutledge. He charged McNeil with taking some unfair advantage of him. The news spread like a delicious ripple, much to the embarrassment of Ann Rutledge herself, who was informed of it by Nance Cameron before sundown.

But the town gossip which went farthest and quickest and was to last longest, started about a week later when John McNeil disposed of his interest in his store and his farm, and suddenly left New Salem.

It was reported that he left town on his best horse, that Mrs.

Rutledge and Ann had seen him off, and that he had said he was going back East to get his family.

"What did he sell the best farm in Sangamon County for if he expected to return? Was he still engaged to Ann Rutledge—or was their engagement broken off? Had Hill had anything to do with it? Or did McNeil think Abe Lincoln liked Ann?" These and many other questions were asked.

Abe Lincoln asked no questions, but for the time Blackstone and Shakespeare, his grammar and his poem were alike forgotten, and he enjoyed the half-fearful sensation of one walking in the dark toward a sunrise.

CHAPTER XXIII

Alias McNeil

Of all the people in New Salem who were surprised at the sudden and mysterious leave-taking of the lover of Ann Rutledge, no one was so mystified and troubled as Ann herself. Especially was she perplexed and troubled about a promise he had exacted from her the last night they were together.

"Ann," he said, "you've promised to marry me—haven't you?"

Ann looked at him questioningly. "Of course—why do you ask such a question?"

"Will you wait for me if I should go away for a time?"

"Surely you believe I will."

"Yes, you'll wait unless Abe Lincoln gets you while I'm away."

"Abe Lincoln," she repeated. "What makes you say that?"

"Abe Lincoln has not been keeping company with any of the girls, and it's not their fault. No more is it natural for a young fellow as full of life as Abe Lincoln as not to like the girls— except when they like *one*. I'm not blind. There's no other girl in New Salem like you; maybe no other one good enough for Abe Lincoln. He'll want something extra on account of his book-learning. Abe's a good fellow, but he's lazy as a dog, always lying around when he ought to be laying by some dollars."

"But he is studying and reading when he is lying around. When anybody's mind is at work they're not lazy."

"You always take up for Abe Lincoln, I notice—ever since the day his ark got stuck on the dam. I suppose it's because he was born under a lucky star."

"What's lucky about Abraham Lincoln?"

"Everything. The way he got to bring the steamboat down the river; the way he got to be captain in the Black Hawk war. And now they say he is certain to go to the Legislature."

"But it's not luck. It's because he can do things. 'I will prepare myself,' he often says, 'and when my chance comes I will be ready.'"

"Yes, that's what he says, and that's exactly the reason he'll get you while I'm away."

"But I have promised you, John."

"Out of sight out of mind," he answered.

"Do you think I would forget a solemn promise?" There was surprise and something of resentment in her tone.

"Not exactly that, though Abe Lincoln could talk black into white if he took a notion. But a fellow don't care to have a girl stick to him just on account of a sacred promise."

"What makes you talk so strangely?" she asked. "And tell me, where are you going? You haven't told me this yet."

"I'm going back where I came from—back where I left my people when I came out here."

"That was in New York somewhere."

"Yes, in New York somewhere. I expect to come back and bring them."

"When are you going?"

"Tomorrow."

"Tomorrow! So soon?" she exclaimed in surprise and pain. "Will you be gone long?"

"Maybe—I don't know how long. But before I go I've a secret to tell you."

"Something you have never told me?"

"Something I have never told anybody. Something you must not tell."

"Not even my mother? I tell her everything."

"Not even your mother, nor father."

"What is it, John?" and Ann's face was troubled as she asked the question.

"You solemnly promise you will not tell—at least not until I come back?"

"I'd like to know what it is before I promise. It doesn't seem right to keep things from Father and Mother. I never do."

"Not even my secrets? Don't you trust me, Ann?"

"Of course I do, John."

"Then promise."

Ann was sorely puzzled. Her lips twitched.

"Promise," he repeated, "and don't cry. It's nothing to cry about."

Still Ann hesitated. "Father would think it strange."

"How can he think it strange if he knows nothing about it?"

"I promise," she said solemnly.

"All right, then, my name is not John McNeil at all."

Ann stared at him a moment. Then with something like a gasp she said, "Your name is not John McNeil? What is it? Who are you?"

"Just this. I came here from—nobody knows just where, not even you, Ann. I named myself John McNeil because I wanted to lose myself."

"What for?" she questioned mechanically.

"Back where I came from my folks are poor—these no-account poor that every enterprising man despises. I wanted to get something together and knew I should never be able to do it if they learned where I was, for I was eternally being called on to help them and keep them from starving when I was where they could call on me."

"Have you heard nothing from them since you came here?"

"Nothing."

"Oh, John! how could you? Perhaps your mother has wanted for something."

"She would have wanted just the same if I had been there."

"She might even be dead."

"I don't think so and hope not. At any rate, I have made some money. Now I'm going back to get the rest of them and I want you to wait for me until I come back. But your name will never be Ann McNeil."

"What will it be?" she asked with pale lips.

"Well," he said, looking at her with a half-smile, "if it's not Mrs. Abraham Lincoln before I return, it will be Mrs. James McNamra."

"James McNamra," she repeated as if puzzled. "I never heard the name."

"It is my name. You will get used to it."

Ann was silent. She was making an effort to choke back great lumps that kept rising in her throat. Then the tears came and ran over the rims of her dark, blue eyes.

"How funny women are," McNeil said. "There's nothing to cry about, and I want to see you laughing the last time."

"I want to tell Mother and Father," she sobbed.

"You said you wouldn't. Are you going to keep your promise?"

"Yes," she answered.

"Then kiss me good night. Tomorrow I will ride past here on my way to Springfield. But there'll be no kissing then. The town folks will have enough to talk about as it is."

After McNeil had left town Ann began watching the post office, and the postmaster rendered her careful help in the matter.

But days went by and no letter came. The fair face of Ann Rutledge took on a worried look, and had it not been for the kindly assistance of the postmaster the gossips might have known more of Ann's correspondence—or lack of it, than they had yet been able to learn.

The strain on Ann, the worst part of it being the secret, which to her was fast coming to seem little short of a crime against her good father and mother, began to tell on her. She laughed little and sang less. She was more seldom seen with the young people.

Mr. and Mrs. Rutledge noticed this, as well as did Abraham Lincoln, and one night, when Ann's face showed that she had been particularly disappointed because of no letter, Abe Lincoln suggested that Ann learn grammar with him out of his highly prized little book. Both Mr. and Mrs. Rutledge accepted the offer as a special favor.

So it happened that Ann and Abe were left together, and with the precious grammar spread on Ann's little worktable they sat down to their task, he on one side, she on the other. The book was not large, and hovering over it, the mop of coarse, black hair all but touched the crown of fine-spun gold.

"I will be the teacher," Abe Lincoln said after they had looked through the book, which was the only one of the kind in New Salem.

"We will now study the verb 'to love,'" and turning the pages he found the place.

"I love," he said, looking across at Ann.

Her eyes were on the book.

"Next is 'You love'?" He spoke the words as a question with the accent on the "you."

"Say it now, Ann, just as I have, and look at your teacher. First, 'I love.'"

"I love," she repeated.

"Might be better," he said. "Now the next, and look at your teacher and repeat after me, 'You love'?"

As Ann repeated the question her face took on a touch of pink.

"Very good—very good, indeed. Now the next is, 'We love.' We will say that together with the accent on the 'we.' Now— one—two—three—'we,'" and he beat three times slowly with his big hand. "Ready, 'We love.'"

There was much more emphasis in the teacher's statement than in that of the pupil. The effect on Ann was to cause a merry laugh. "Ann," said Abe Lincoln, "I'm goin' to give you this grammar. I know it by heart—by heart, Ann—especially the verb 'I love.' I want you to learn it"; and he wrote across the top,

"Ann Rutledge is learning grammar," and pushed it across the table to her.

"What a splendid present!" she said with a smiling face. "How I wish I had something to give you, Abraham—would you take my little Bible—and read it?"

"Oh, Ann!—would you give it to me?" he asked with the joy of a child.

"You won't give it away like you did the muffler, will you?"

"Wouldn't you be willin' if I should run across a bigger sinner than Abe Lincoln?" he answered, laughing.

From a chest of drawers she took a little brown book and handed it to him.

"It must be marked, Ann." And, taking the pencil he had written on the grammar with, he handed it to her, saying, "Now we will find a place where the verb 'to love' is found."

The quick ease with which he turned to the passage he had in mind surprised Ann. With the open page before him he said, "You are religious, Ann. You obey the commands of the Holy Scriptures, don't you?"

"I try to."

"And you'll do anything in reason you are told to by the Book?"

"Yes, indeed."

"Take your pencil and mark this"; and, with his long forefinger pointing to the text, he read impressively, " 'This is my commandment, that you love one another.' "

Whether in the Scriptures or out of it, Ann and Abe soon found something to laugh at. "Ann is laughing," Mr. Rutledge said to his wife. "How good it sounds! What on earth has been the matter with her?"

"She hasn't heard from John McNeil," Mrs. Rutledge answered.

"McNeil seems to be a good fellow and unusually successful," James Rutledge observed after a moment of reflection, "but Ann's not married to him yet."

CHAPTER XXIV

In the Cellar

After months of waiting Ann Rutledge received a letter from John McNeil. It was a straightforward explanation of the delay, mentioning sickness along the way, and other obstacles.

Ann Rutledge was delighted. In some way it seemed to lift a burden and answer a question.

Nance Cameron had the pleasure of starting the news of the letter, and its satisfactory contents, which allayed gossip, and for a time Ann was quite herself again. But no more letters came, and Ann was soon again cast down by the strangeness of her lover's silence. Once when she had hurried to the post office after the weekly mail had arrived only to be told by the postmaster there was no letter, she made an appeal to him which touched his heart.

"He ought to write to me," she half sobbed. "Everybody is wondering about it. I don't want people to know he never writes. Don't tell it."

The postmaster promised, but Ann's troubled face haunted him, and he found himself getting thoroughly indignant with McNeil, even though glad beyond expression that he was treating her just as he was.

As the days and weeks went by Ann found the burden of the secret weighing heavily on her conscience, and the thought kept intruding itself that since he had deceived her in one way he might have done so in other ways. It was hard to think this, and yet it was almost as easy to believe as that his name was not McNeil and that he had been gone months without writing. She felt that she had done very wrong to promise to keep a secret, and such a grave and important secret, from her parents. Yet she had promised, and, torn between the feeling that she must confide in her parents and that she must keep her promise, she grew pale and quiet and unlike the laughing, singing Ann of a few months previous. Her parents noticed this with concern, and it hurt the heart of Abe Lincoln, yet none of them surmised the real trouble.

One day after Ann had been her unreal self for several months, Lincoln came home for supper early and went into the kitchen to help Mrs. Rutledge.

"I want a pan of potatoes," she said. "They're in the short bin near the door. I sent Ann for them half an hour ago, but she must have gone somewhere else."

"Mrs. Rutledge," said Abe Lincoln as he tucked the pan under his arm, "what ails Ann?"

"I'm sure I don't know. Her father and I have wondered. It's something about John McNeil, I think. I suppose she's heard the talk. I can't understand John McNeil. He's too fine a young fellow to do anything mean, I'm sure. I hope James Rutledge don't turn against him. He's slow to rile up, but the fur flies when he does get mad. Run on now after the taters."

Abe Lincoln made his way down the cellar steps softly. The door was not closed. As he entered he thought he saw some object move in one of the dark corners. Opening the door a little more he looked into the dark. When his eyes had become accustomed to the gloom, he saw the outlines of a human figure huddled together, and putting down his pan, with shoulders and head bent, he walked over the hard earthen floor to the dark corner,

Here he found Ann Rutledge sitting on the edge of a turnip-box with her head leaning against the log and earthen wall.

"Ann—Ann Rutledge," he said softly. A sob was his only answer.

"Ann—Ann," he said, bending over her.

"Go away, please," she said.

"No, I will not go away. You are in trouble. I want to help you."

"You cannot—nobody can help me," and again her voice was choked with sobs.

"Of course somebody can help you. Tell me about it. Perhaps I can help you."

"But I cannot tell—my trouble—is—is—a secret."

"A secret," Lincoln said, "a secret—who from?"

"From everybody in the world but John McNeil. I promised him I would not tell—not even my mother."

"He got you to swear to a secret you could not confide in your mother?" and Lincoln seemed aghast.

"Yes—and I never had a secret from Father and Mother before."

"Ann—Ann Rutledge!" and Lincoln's voice was no longer gentle; "a secret from a girl's mother is never the right kind of a secret. A mother is the one person on earth no honorable man would want secrets kept from. It is wrong, Ann—wrong."

"I believe it is. It is wearing me out—it is breaking my heart —I feel that I cannot keep it—and yet I promised."

"Ann Rutledge!" Lincoln was bending over her and there was a tone in his voice that compelled her to look up. In the gloom his face had taken on a strange, white cast and something of the expression it had borne when Jack Armstrong had tried the unfair trick.

"Ann Rutledge," he whispered under his breath, "has John McNeil in any way wronged you? If he has—if he has—I—will choke the life out of him, and that without warnin'."

"Oh, Abraham!" she cried, "don't talk so. I don't know whether he has wronged me or not. That's what the secret's about—I don't know and I wish I could die right here in this cellar," and again she turned her face to the wall and sobbed.

Speechless, Abraham Lincoln looked down upon her. His face was pale, his teeth set—his great fists were clenched, yet what could he do?

The sobs of the girl beat against his heart, strongly fanning the pain and fierce passion.

"What shall I do—what shall I do?" she said brokenly.

"You shall go straight to your mother," he said firmly. "Tell her everything."

"But I promised—gave an honorable promise, a solemn promise that I would not tell."

"There can be no such thing as an honorable promise to the kind of a man who does not know the meanin' of the word. There can be no such thing as a sacred promise to a man who has no more conception of sacredness than a beast. The man who has brought you to this trouble, of whatever kind it may be, is unfit for consideration. Go to your mother. If you don't go *I'll carry you there in my arms.*"

A moment she hesitated. Then she arose. He twined his fingers around her arm and without speaking they crossed the cellar. At the door she paused. "Come on, Ann," he said, and they went up the steps together.

Entering the kitchen, Abe Lincoln said, "I found your little girl in the cellar—in trouble. She has come to tell her mother about it. I'll go fetch the potatoes."

CHAPTER XXV

Father and Daughter

After Ann Rutledge confided her heart-troubling secret to her mother, Mrs. Rutledge lost no time in laying the matter before her husband. She feared it would be hard to make him see that John McNeil's conduct toward Ann had been honorable, and James Rutledge believed in the kind of honor that makes a man's word as good as his bond, and would take advantage of no situation to perpetrate an injustice.

He listened in silence as Mrs. Rutledge told him Ann's secret, the secret that was changing the glad-hearted girl into a quiet, nervous woman. Several times he seemed about to speak. He listened, however, until the end, but Mrs. Rutledge knew he was angry.

"Now, James," she counseled, "don't be too hard on John McNeil. What he said may all be true. He may go back and get his people and bring them right here as he said."

"Maybe he will—but does that change the fact that he played double? Does that change the fact that during his years of plenty he has never helped those of his own flesh and blood who may have suffered? John McNeil is as cold a trade driver as ever hit the trail to the West, and if he comes back here——"

"Now, James, be careful. Aside from the awful effect the whole thing has had on poor Ann, there may be no real sin committed."

"Aside from the effect on our Ann? My God! how much more sin could a man commit unless he had ruined her reputation— and if he had done that——" and James Rutledge arose and paced the floor.

"But he didn't. How can you let such a thought come into your head about Ann? Don't get yourself all worked up over a straw man."

"Straw man?" he exclaimed angrily. "Is it a straw man that our Ann laughs no more? Is it a straw man that we never hear her singing home across the bluffs? Is it a straw man that her sweet face has been taking on lines of worry, ill fitting the face of Ann Rutledge? Is it a straw man that she was forced into a promise to keep a secret—a dishonorable secret—from her own father and mother? There's no straw man about any such thing as this."

James Rutledge sat down and lit his pipe. After it was smoking well, Mrs. Rutledge said, "What shall I say to Ann?"

"Tell Ann to come to me," he said shortly.

Mrs. Rutledge went out, and a moment later Ann came. When she entered the room her father was standing with his back to the fireplace, his hands behind him.

"Yes, Father," she said quietly.

James Rutledge surveyed her a moment. What he was thinking of, she had no time to consider, but the expression on his face seemed to be a combination of wrath and pity, of love and outraged justice.

"A man called John McNeil asked my consent to marry you, Ann."

"Yes, Father." Her voice was a trifle unsteady.

"I supposed him to be the honorable and straight-faced young gentleman he seemed to be."

She made no reply. James Rutledge blew out a couple of puffs of smoke.

"From your mother I have just learned that there is no such person as John McNeil."

"No, Father."

"This McNamra, or whoever he may be, may turn up in these parts again some time."

"I don't know"; and the tremor had not left her voice.

"He might have the unmitigated hardihood to expect to marry the daughter of James Rutledge, the girl he courted under the name of McNeil. If he should—if he should come back and should even look like he thought of such a thing—I would— would——"

"Father," Ann said softly, stepping nearer him, for she saw that he was angry, "you wouldn't do anything wrong."

"Wrong?" he said. "Wrong—no—nothing wrong—what I'd do would be right"; and he turned and knocked his pipe against the chimney with such force as to threaten its existence.

"Perhaps he was telling the truth. Perhaps he will return some day just as he said he would."

"Perhaps—perhaps. But is he telling the truth about his name? No, he is lying. One way or another he has lied to a woman, and a man who will desert his own father and mother would desert his wife. I'm not condemning him too hard, but he will never marry James Rutledge's daughter. Do you understand, Ann?"

"Yes, Father." Her voice was unsteady.

"He has put you in a most embarrassing position—more than you know. You will be talked about when his double life is known, and, since it is bound to come out, the sooner the better, and I shall see to that. Gossips will discuss matters that's none of their business, but they will not go too far, my girl, for James Rutledge is your father."

"Perhaps I will hear from him—even yet," she said with an effort.

"If you do, hand the letter to me. I'll give the young man some advice about swearing dutiful daughters to keep secrets from their parents."

The tears which Ann had struggled to keep back now stood in her eyes, and she feared to speak lest the slightest movement of her face would start them running down her cheeks.

James Rutledge looked at her. The expression on his stern face changed instantly, and the voice was wonderfully softened as he said, "Ann, my little girl, don't cry. Don't waste good tears. It's not too late to mend the harm. Tonight when you say your prayers add a couple of lines telling your Creator that the best thing He has done for you up to this good time is to save you from being the wife of a man whose word would have no other meaning to you than so much noise. Run on now, my girl, and tell your mother I'd like to see her."

CHAPTER XXVI

Gloom and the Light

Ann's secret was not long in gaining publicity after her father found it out, nor was he disposed entirely to discredit the gossips' reports that McNeil's strange actions might be due to a living wife or some crime committed. Why else on earth would a man change his name, desert a girl like Ann Rutledge, and go away—nobody knew where?

The town gossip greatly embarrassed Ann Rutledge, yet she was glad she had told her parents, and, the burden of the secret now being removed, she was more like herself.

The action of John McNeil and the consequent displeasure of Ann's father were much to the liking of Lincoln, and while he felt sorry for Ann, his sorrow was not sufficient to hold back his joy, which was given expression in the jolliest stories he had ever told. Laughter seemed infectious around the post office when the postmaster was there. His days in New Salem had all been busy, happy days with his good friends, and opportunities for study. But better than all was the growing consciousness that an undefined hope which had been struggling against a clearly defined duty, was approaching the right of way. His heart was glad as he went about over the country with his stakes and chains.

It was just about this time that the wheel of fortune turned. The men who had bought the Lincoln and Berry store and had given Lincoln paper to pay his debts with, closed their doors one day without notice, and, without saying farewell to a soul in New Salem, disappeared.

When Lincoln heard this he felt slip upon him the burden of a debt that staggered him. Not in a lifetime did it seem he would be able to pay it. And so it was that just as it seemed that he was about to enter the path of a golden glow he was thrown, instead, into the black gloom of a great despondency.

When the word was passed around town of Abe Lincoln's bad luck there was much talk. What would he do? There seemed to be just two alternatives—to skin out and leave it all, as the men had done who bought the store, and his partner Berry before them had done, or to settle down to a lifetime of struggle and pay the debt. Everybody believed Abe Lincoln thoroughly honest, but here was a test that seemed beyond the powers of human endurance.

The night the store was closed, Abe Lincoln did not come home to supper.

"Where is Abe Lincoln?" the Rutledges asked.

Nobody knew. Ann slipped away to the post office. It was closed. She rattled the door and called his name at the latch-hole but received no answer.

Day was drawing to a close, but she made an excuse to go to the mill, and with a little basket on her arm she hurried down the sloping road. Twilight shades were falling over the weather-stained log building which seemed to be drawing itself into the shadows of the trees on the opposite bank of the river. The big stone wheel was silent, but the waters falling over the dam gave out the sound of something alive.

Quietly she approached the wide mill doors which stood open. On the threshold she looked carefully in. For a moment the deeper gloom of the inside blinded her. Then the big white millstone took shape, and the door, opening onto the river platform. Through this a pale light filtered.

Taking a step farther in, she looked again toward some dark outlines which she was sure were not those of pillar or prop, outlines which took the form of a tall, shadowy giant standing against the doorway and looking out upon the river in the falling darkness.

She crossed the mill rapidly and softly, and, approaching the tall shadowy figure, touched the giant of the gloom on the arm and said, "Abraham Lincoln."

He turned about quickly. "Ann—Ann Rutledge—what are you doing here?"

"I have been looking for you."

"Why?"

"You did not come to supper."

"I often go without supper."

"I heard of your trouble. I wanted to find you and to help you. You found me in the cellar—and helped me."

"And what can you do—what can anyone do for me?" and he turned again to the river. "Look at the darkness. Only *that* for me."

"But light always follows darkness, Abraham. God has planned it so. Sometimes the night is very dark, and very long, but morning comes. It is always so."

He was silent and they stood together in the gloom.

"God!" he said to himself. "Is there a God? I wonder. If there is a God He knows how hard I've tried—worked against fate itself, how I wanted to be something in the world. I've loved to study about Washington and have been fool enough to dream I might do something for my country some time. But Washington came from a race of cavaliers. I come from the poorest of ten thousand. Washington at the age of twenty-one was an Adjutant General of Virginia with the rank of major. Abraham Lincoln at twenty-one was driving two yoke of oxen to an emigrant wagon through the mud holes and wilds of the West and had never been to school a year in his life. I was tryin'. I felt that I was gettin' ahead. Now comes a burden that will crush me to earth—for, Ann Rutledge—Ann Rutledge," and he turned toward her and spoke with fierce determination, "every penny of this debt must be paid if it takes me *to the day of my death* with my coffin money thrown in."

"Yes, Abraham Lincoln," she answered gently, "every penny —and God will help you do it, for God never expects the impossible. He's not that kind of a God, you know."

"You talk about God," said Lincoln rather indifferently, "as if you were sure—well, I believe you are. I knew it the night I heard you singin' on the bluff. I have heard you sing that song many times since—sometimes in my dreams. I wish I could feel as you do when you sing your pilgrim song. I have imagined that I will some day, but now—now I think of my mother lyin' under a forgotten tangle where strange beasts creep. She was a pilgrim, too—but she passed out of it all weak and weary. Yet she believed just as you believe, as I have tried to believe."

"But, Abraham—you know we are here for just a little time. The song says, 'I can tarry—I can tarry but a night.' Sometimes the night is very short, as when a child passes on. Sometimes it is longer, as when an old, old man dies. But whether long or short, the night gives way to the morning with its light and fresh life and strength. I know it is so."

She had been speaking in a quiet voice with a touch of pleading, for she felt he was not paying close attention.

"How do you know it?" he asked, turning to her. "Tell me how you know it—or why you believe so strongly."

"Let us sit down," she said, "here where the light is fading on the river. See, only the foam shines now. But in just a little while the moon will put a thousand bars of silver on the water. We are not afraid of the dark—you and I—nor of each other. I want to tell you a story."

He was paying attention now. They sat down on the broad step of the mill door. To him Ann Rutledge had never been so close before, and yet just now so unattainable. Never before had she spoken to him in such childish simplicity, yet now she was mysteriously beyond his understanding.

"I have often doubted," he said, with something like a sigh

as he stretched his legs across the platform and waited; "I should like to believe—as you do. Can you make me?"

"I will tell you a story," she said again. Her voice was low and sweet. It seemed in tune with the gathering darkness, the falling of the water, the evening calm and the burdened heart of the man.

"When I was yet very small I began wondering and asking questions about things I could neither understand nor believe. It was while we were back in Kentucky I was sent to the pasture to watch the cows. There was a pond in the low end of the pasture where the reeds grew and where all was very quiet around. I was sitting beside the water, wondering perhaps if something strange and beautiful would appear from its depths as in fairy stories, when I saw a hideous, mud-colored grub creeping slowly above the waterline and climbing the reed. I was tempted to knock it back out of sight, it was so ugly. But I only watched. Very soon its muddy shell cracked open, something with wings crept out and the shell fell back to the place from which it had come. The new creature spread its wings slowly. They dried, turning as they did so into silver gauze, which he spread out like bits of shining lace. Then he went skimming away across the pond and over the dandelions and grass flowers, even over the heads of the grazing cows. In all my life I had never dreamed of anything so wonderful nor had any fairy story ever been told me that was so marvelous as what I had just seen. I looked back to the pond. A ray of sun was shining so that I could see the bottom. The cast-off shell was lying there in the mud. There were others like it around, except they had life in them. They crept up and maybe looked at the empty shell. One touched it and turned away.

"After a time the new creature with the silvery wings came again and rested on the reed. His reflection showed in the water. Perhaps he could see those who were as he had been, creeping in the mud. But he had no way of telling them that they would one day become creatures of the upper world of sunshine and flowers and sky, for the only world they knew was mud. And then I thought of people—and that we are yet dwelling in the world of mud. The Bible calls it the 'earth.' It says, 'There is a natural body . . .'—do you remember—'There is a natural body and there is a spiritual body. The first is of the earth—earthy.' And it is not until we have left the old body that we can know the life on wings—the life up in God's big fields of sunshine that we call heaven.

"As I watched the shining creature sitting on the reed, I thought perhaps it was a mother wishing she could tell her child down below to be brave and not mind the mud, for at longest it can last but a little while. Of course there was no way the one could speak and the other hear. But it was a helpful thought. Do you ever think of your mother this way? Do you ever feel when you are in the gloom that she is not very far away, and only waiting until you have been changed, to tell you many things? The Bible calls it, 'When this mortal shall have put on Immortality . . .'"

"Immortality," the man repeated, as if to himself. It was the title of the new poem he so liked. Then he said, almost reverently, "Go on, Ann."

"*I believe,*" she said simply, "that's why I am so happy when I'm singing 'I'm a pilgrim.' It is my soul you hear singing, Abraham—*that part of me that will not die,* that is shouting on the way. Wasn't God good to plan it all so lovely?"

Abraham Lincoln turned slowly and looked down on Ann Rutledge.

The moon was throwing its first gleams across the river. In the pale light the face and hair with its pale red-gold halo seemed to stand out from the shadowy background like something ethereal and unreal. The man gazed at it. It was so shining—so happy.

"You were sobbin' in the cellar not so long ago," he said.

"That was the darkness—but always the light comes back."

"Because you believe."

"Don't you believe? Oh, you must believe, Abraham."

"Do you want to help me to believe? Do you want to help

me to reach the heights—higher heights than man has ever climbed? For I feel that you can help me do even this. You can transform me, and I do not expect to die either—not yet."

"What can I do for you?"

"Once I saw an eagle rise from a bluff on the river. Easily it lifted itself above everything and soared against the sky. So was I lifted up when I heard you singin' on the heights. All night long I sat thinkin' about it. I could not fathom the mystery then. With the sunrise the matin' call of the bird began to unfold the mystery to me. Ann—Ann Rutledge, I want you to let me love you."

"Does love have to be let?" She asked the question, looking out across the water and woods.

"No—never. But dams can be built, and then the waters on their way must do one of two things—break the dam or change their course. I do not want to change my course. I do not want to break a dam—if it can be helped—for I'll make a ripsnortin' big smash-up of it if I do. May I love you?"

He was looking into her face, which was still shining.

"Let me get a letter to John McNeil asking him to release me."

"And then, Ann?"

"Then—oh, Abraham Lincoln!—*then*—but we mustn't even talk of it yet." She arose from the step.

The tall man stood beside her. The rising moon cast a light on his face. The girl looked at it in wonderment.

"Abraham," she said, "you do not look like the same man I found here."

"Keep still, Ann," he whispered. "We are just outside heaven."

"And you believe now—believe?" and she waited for his answer.

"Believe, yes, I believe. I must believe in the *Great Creator*. Nothin' less could have fashioned the soul of Ann Rutledge. From now on, eternally, I shall believe to my soul's salvation."

"Out of the gloom into the light," she said softly.

A few moments they stood as if not wishing to break some

magic spell. Then he said, "You must run right home. We will not go out together; but from the door I will watch until you are well away, then I will follow."

Another moment they tarried in the wide mill door as if loath to leave, then she went out.

As she did so, a small, dark figure stepped around the corner of the mill. The next moment the voices of Davy and Sis Rutledge were heard calling, "Ann—Ann Rutledge!"

"So that's the Mollie that ain't at the mill for no corn grindin'," the small man around the mill said to himself when Ann had answered the call. "Now who's the other bat?"

A moment later the tall figure of Abe Lincoln emerged from the building and turned toward the hill.

"Eh-eh-eh!" grunted the man behind the corner. "He's a bar— he's a bar," and he slapped his foxed breeches and walked half-way up the hill with his coon-skin cap squeezed tightly under his arm as an expression of his joy.

CHAPTER XXVII

Covering the Coals

When James Rutledge was consulted about the sending of Ann's proposed letter asking for a release from her engagement to John McNeil, he said, "What for? Hasn't he released you enough yet? He'll never answer it."

"Don't be too hard on him, James," Mrs. Rutledge said. "He always seemed to know about manners."

"Men have been killed for having no worse manners," Rutledge said dryly.

"But we wouldn't want to be anything but fair," Ann pleaded.

James Rutledge looked at her a moment. Then he reached out his hand and placed it on her red-gold hair.

"Poor little, tender-hearted goose," he said, moving his hand up and down in awkward pats. "Go ahead if it will make you feel any better."

So the letter was written, and approved by James Rutledge. Ann wrapped it in stout brown paper, tied it carefully with string, her father gave her the money to pay its way, and the postmaster mailed it for her.

After the letter had been gone several weeks Ann began watching for a reply. Abe Lincoln also watched, and though no comment was made, the matter was of tremendous importance to both of them.

The spring of 1834 rapidly passed into summer. In the home and garden Ann and her mother were busy every day, while with Abe Lincoln time had never seemed to go so fast. His surveying was taking him farther and farther into the county. In every locality he made new friends. His work was bringing him some money also and he had begun to make payments on the giant debt which hung over him. The entire town considered him little less than a hero, one of those uncommon heroes whose valor lies in simple honesty.

Several of the unhappy experiences of debt came to him, however, for his payments were of necessity slow, and once he was sued at the law and was compelled to turn over his horse and watch—two necessaries he had secured. Friends, however, helped him get them back.

As the citizens of New Salem had before determined, Lincoln was nominated for the Legislature, and during the summer, as he went about his surveying, he used every opportunity to get acquainted with the people. "I must understand the people," he would say to James Rutledge. "I must come in contact with the people. *It is the will of the great mass of common people, not the preference of the favored few, that makes Democracy.*"

To the end of accomplishing this he took time to get acquainted everywhere, sometimes telling stories, sometimes going into fields and lending a hand at gathering in the harvest. But always his honesty, sincerity and hearty sympathy with the toiler, and his big, glad hand of fellowship won him friends, and often after he had told James Rutledge of his travels the older man would say to his wife, "Abe's going to make something of himself. I don't know what. But he's got the stuff in him."

There was much interest in the election. His opponent did not now charge him with being an infidel. The pioneer citizens of Sangamon County were rigidly against the union of Church and State and Abe Lincoln had them well informed concerning the perils of a republic if this foundation stone of democratic government should be stolen or cheated from them. Nor would it have been easy in and about New Salem to make the impression that Abe Lincoln was devoid of religion.

When the voting was over and Abe Lincoln was safely elected, there was a celebration in New Salem out of all proportion to the size of the village, and one of the proudest and happiest of all the shouting, cheering crowd was Ann Rutledge whose face had taken on again its old-time gladness.

During the campaigning time Abe Lincoln had seen little of Ann, and the letter which she had long looked for had not come.

It was after the election excitement had subsided that Abe Lincoln found an evening for Ann. Early after supper the family sat about the fire, and Davy and Sis and Sonny were loath to go to bed, for they had not seen their good friend much of late. But they moved out when James Rutledge bade them, and after a half hour of conversation Mr. and Mrs. Rutledge gave the room to Ann and Abe.

"Don't forget to cover the coals, Ann," her mother had said as she left the room.

"Where's the book? I haven't read my poem for a long time," Abe Lincoln said when they were alone.

Ann took the book from her table drawer and found the poem entitled "Immortality." Lincoln read a few verses.

"It doesn't say much about immortality—does it?" Ann asked.

"Not much, but it means it, because, of course, the souls of men and women do not wither and die like the leaves of the willow and the oak. But I should never have known the meaning—the full, sure meanin' of the word, nor have entered into the better spirit of the poem, if it had not been for you, Ann Rutledge."

"I am glad if I have helped you, but put the book way. Let's tell our fortunes in the fire."

Lincoln put the book on the table and stirred up a bed of glowing coals. Then, side by side, they looked into the future.

"Look," she said, "at the lines just there. I have a long lifeline —so long I must be going to live a hundred years."

He laughed.

"And yours is long. And right in there, there is a wedding— and over there are one, two, three—at least half a dozen children for me." She laughed and stirred the coals again. "This now is your fortune. I see journeys and lots of people. I believe I see the capitol building at Vandalia. Maybe you are going to be a great judge or some state official." She stirred again, but this time she turned and said, "I've always wished, Abraham, that you knew some love stories."

"I do," he answered promptly.

"You?" and she opened her blue eyes wide.

"Yes—the best in the world."

"Where did you get them? You never read storybooks."

"The best books and the greatest books in the world are full of love stories. In fact, Ann, if love and love stories were taken out there wouldn't be anything left for the other fellow to write a book about."

"How about Blackstone—couldn't he write a book?"

"No. In a world without love there would be no matin' in the springtime and no people to write about."

"I didn't mean that. I was talking about just plain love stories."

"So am I. I've read Shakespeare. Did you ever hear his love story about Antony and Cleopatra? It's one of the greatest love stories in the world. She went to him in a wonderful golden barge with purple silk sails and flower-decked maidens dancin' under its Tyrian purple canopies. Little boats swarmed all about it, burnin' incense so that it was wafted on the water in perfumed breezes. This was the ship the fairy Egyptian went to Antony in. Theirs was the love stronger than death. We will read it some time."

"I like it—tell me more."

"You know the love stories in the Bible: the one about Ruth and Boaz, a little out of place these times, but good for its day.

You know the unruly passion that caused poor old Samson's downfall, a love affair in which he loved fiercely but not wisely. But the story that to my mind means more than them all, is the story about Jesus and Mary."

"Oh, Abraham!" she said with a start. "You don't mean that Jesus loved Mary."

"Of course He did. Didn't He love everybody? What else can you make of the incident where Mary, so anxious to show her love in some unusual way, went to the dinner where she emptied her vase of costly perfumes on His hair and feet? Do you remember that her act immediately called forth unkind comments and the sort of criticism that hurts a gentle woman beyond the power of words to tell? What did Jesus do? Did He sit by, dumb like a coward and let her feelin's be wounded when, whether wisely or unwisely, she had sought to prove her love? Was He afraid of those sharp-tongued men? I tell you, Ann, every time I read the story, this Jesus the world loves looms up bigger and grander and more heroic and sublime! Such tender consideration as He showed marks a man, a man. Do you remember what He said as she sat with her eyes full of tears before those men? 'Let her alone,' He said. Then He spoke the few words which were forever to link the name of Mary with that of Jesus, even as He prophesied."

While Ann was considering this somewhat new view of an old story her mother's voice was heard calling, "Don't forget to cover the coals, Ann."

Ann reached for the shovel.

"Not yet," he said, taking her hand and moving his chair closer to hers. She did not try to withdraw her hand from the large one that held it.

For a moment he sat looking into the fire. Then he turned to her. "Ann," he said in a low voice, and unsteady, "Ann Rutledge, look at me. I have something to say to you."

Ann turned her face to his. For a moment he seemed to search it with a gaze as tender as it was masterful and as pleading as it was secure.

"We are goin' to cover the coals," he said. "Do you know, Ann, that hearts are hearthstones where women keep the live fire burnin'? My hearthstone has been ash-strewn and cold—with nobody to cover the coals?"

She felt the large hand around hers tighten its grasp, but he yet looked into the fire.

When he spoke again it was with a different tone. The pleading was gone. There was a tone of masterful security in it.

"Ann," he said, "we have been waitin' for a letter. It has not come. The time is now past when one or ten thousand letters refusin' to release you would avail anything. When a man loves a woman as I love you, it is his God-ordained privilege to get her. Do you understand? I *love* you. I have loved you since before I ever saw your face. It came to me the night I heard you singin' on the heights. I love you more than anything on earth or in heaven and I feel some way that love like this can come but once. I *love* you and I would give my life to have you mine—to cover the coals on the hearthstone of my heart."

There was such an intensity in his voice, in his face, as Ann had never seen. There was a pleading hunger, there was a suppressed mastery that she was conscious of. She did not take her eyes from his face. "Ann," and without letting go of her hand he arose and drew her up before him, "together we stand at the most momentous time of all our lives—do you love me?"

"Do I love you?" Ann half whispered with a smile that turned her face radiant; meantime her eyes grew shining with tears. The next instant she felt those long arms around her that Ole Bar had hinted would be useful in mating season, felt them binding her slender body so close she could hear the rapid thumping of his heart, and he kissed her with the savage joy of sweet possession, and, cradling her face in his strong hand, he held her cheek against his and breathed the fierce and tender joy words could not tell.

"Oh, Abraham," she whispered, "do you love me so much—so *very* much."

"Love you?" he said half defiantly. "You cannot know, for

you have not starved for it as I have. I love you, Ann Rutledge—not for a week or a month, or a year, but until this mortal shall have put on immortality; for if souls are immortal as you have taught me, *love is eternal.*"

A moment longer they stood in each other's arms. Then he held her away from him, looked at her and in serious tones said, "Sing for me, Ann—just one stanza of that good old hymn, 'This is the way I long have sought.'"

"Hear Ann," Mrs. Rutledge said to her husband as the old-time music of happy laughter sounded on the stillness of the night.

"Good for Abe!" he answered drowsily; "let them alone."

CHAPTER XXVIII

"He's Ruint Hisself Forever"

There was no one in New Salem surprised when it began to be whispered about that Abe Lincoln was setting up to Ann Rutledge.

Indeed that seemed quite the natural thing. Both were favorites. Both were different in some ways from any others, perhaps superior, and both were everybody's friends. The wonderful change in Ann, too, was a source of pleasure to all who knew her, for she had not been able to hide the disappointment and embarrassment through which she had passed.

Abe Lincoln had always been fairly happy so far as any one knew. He seemed even more happy now, and quite naturally the people charged this to Ann Rutledge, and the two words, "Ann and Abe," began to be everywhere linked together. It was not until Thanksgiving, however, that any definite announcement was made. This was at a dinner, the biggest and jolliest ever given in New Salem.

"Mother," James Rutledge had said to his wife, "the increase has been fair, but we've more than increase to be thankful for. Ann's got back to herself again. Fact, there never was a time in all her life when her singing sounded so good to me as now, and

she laughs as if there were no such thing in the world as trouble.
Then I'm not sorry she and Abe fixed things up. Abe Lincoln's
got some future, sure as two and two make four. It does seem
outside the bounds of all reason that a young backwoodsman
that never went to school and has had more hard knocks than
ten men generally stands up under, could ever get to be Governor of Illinois. Yet who knows—who knows?"

"James," Mrs. Rutledge answered, "you're getting visionary.
Just 'cause you like Abe Lincoln uncommon well and he's going
to marry our Ann ain't any sign he'll ever get to any such exalted
position as governor."

"I don't know. He's doing fairly—fairly. He's the youngest
member in the Legislature. His life is before him. He's going to
finish law next year, and Major Stuart says there's no man, old
or young, in this state today that knows the Constitution like
Abe Lincoln. He may never get there, but I'd not die of surprise if he did. And I'm waiting with interest to see what stand
he takes down at Vandalia. But getting back to Thanksgiving,
we have uncommon things to be thankful for. Abe has no home
and like as not nobody ever had a dinner for him. Let Abe and
Ann have a dinner and invite in some of the young people."

This plan suited Mrs. Rutledge. Abe and Ann were delighted
and preparations were at once begun. There were mince and
pumpkin pies, and cakes and plum pudding to be baked, and
the tenderest pig and the biggest turkey on the farm were to be
roasted. The cellar and storehouse were raided and in the woods
Ann had the good fortune to find a vine with shining leaves
and blue-black berries which she twined about a great bouquet
of evergreen set in a frame of shining red apples in the middle
of the table.

Abe stayed near Ann, and once when she was making pastry
for jam tarts he kissed her, until, in self-defense, she powdered
his black hair white with her flour-dusted hands, and Mrs. Rutledge laughed until she had to rest her ample body in an easy
chair.

This incident was not long in getting out, for Nance, who was present, told it at singing-school, and it was passed around with as genuine a feeling of pleasure as if those telling it were themselves being kissed.

"I've been looking for just this kind of love affair for Abe Lincoln," Hannah Armstrong said. "The kind that's taking up with everything that swings petticoats only has skin-deep cases, but there's others has bone cases. When it gets in the bone, ain't any use ever trying to get it out."

The afternoon before Thanksgiving, Abe Lincoln announced that he was going to Springfield on an important mission. What it was he told nobody but Ann's mother. Ann had an idea the mission had something to do with the festivities of the next day, but no hint was dropped as to what it was.

With Thanksgiving came the dinner and the merriment about the long table of laughing and storytelling with jokes about Ann and Abe, for as yet the progress of their courtship was not definitely known.

Abe and Ann had been put side by side in two chairs which Nance and other girls had decorated with strings of popcorn and sprigs of green. When the dinner was at last over, Abe arose and, stretching himself to his full height and stepping behind Ann's chair, said, "There are all sorts of Thanksgivin's and all sorts of things to be thankful for. But there will never be another one like this, for I have asked Ann Rutledge, the sweetest girl in all the world, to be my wife, and she has done me the honor of givin' me her promise. I have here a little band of gold to be put on that finger which it is said sends the channels of its blood directest to the heart. It has words inside which carry the world's greatest message. Hold out your hand, Ann."

The speech was a surprise. Every eye was turned on Ann as Abe Lincoln took her hand and slipped the little band on her third finger. James Rutledge leaned eagerly forward. Immediately there was a great clapping of hands and then the young people gathered around Ann to see the ring and to learn the message that Abe had had put in the ring.

"Read it Ann—read it," they cried.

And Ann, her face shining with joy and pink with blushes, read, "Love is eternal."

She looked at Abraham Lincoln. Their eyes met a moment, then he bent down and kissed her, and again the young companions shouted and laughed, and when there were none of them looking his way, Ann's father wiped his eyes.

Just a few days later Abraham Lincoln made ready to go to Vandalia, seventy-five miles from New Salem, to represent Sangamon County. As usual he had no money, but he had no trouble borrowing enough to buy a cheap suit, which was the best, however, he had as yet put on his back. James Rutledge furnished the horse, and Ann and her mother looked after his simple outfit.

"Abraham," Ann said when she surveyed him in his new suit, "you look so nice, only your tie is crooked."

He pulled it around, saying, "Such a nuisance. What are they good for, anyhow?"

Ann laughed. "You've got it as far out of line under your left ear now as you had it before under the right," she said. "Let me fix it for you." Stepping on a footstool she motioned him to stand before her, and straightened his tie.

"Abraham," she said in despair before he left the house, "it's crooked again—your tie."

"Let it alone," was his answer. "The tie is all right. It's my neck that's crooked."

After he had gone Ann began spinning, piecing quilts and hemming linen in preparation for a spring wedding.

Both James Rutledge and Ann heard from Sangamon County's representative. To the father he wrote that he was forming a plan to have the state capitol moved from Vandalia to Springfield, in his opinion a much better point than the small place down the country. What he wrote to Ann nobody asked. Sometimes she let her father and mother read the letters. Once James Rutledge read, "I am glad you are so well—so strong, so happy, my little pilgrim. The world is a new world, Ann, now that I have you. I feel some insistent force pushing me on to something —I do not know what. But with the love of a woman like you, there are no heights a man dare not reach out for."

Meantime discussion in New Salem about Lincoln kept up. Almost every man in town was of the opinion that Abe was going to be somebody, but they all waited to see what he would stand for in this, his first experience, as representative of the people.

It came at last. Abraham Lincoln had gone on record in favor of woman suffrage and against slavery.

When this news was told in the little group of which Ole Bar happened to be one, he was for a moment struck dumb with disappointment. Then with impressive profanity he burst out, "A bar would have more sense. Couldn't he find nothin' in Vandalyer to take up but wimmin and niggers? He's ruint hisself forever."

CHAPTER XXIX

God's Little Girl

Early in the spring James Rutledge decided to move from Rutledge Inn to his farm about seven miles beyond New Salem.

Mrs. Rutledge and Ann suffered the pangs of heart that come to women when they must leave homes made dear by the birth of children and of love. Aside from the sentiment, however, Mrs. Rutledge was glad to change to farm life, for inn-keeping had been hard for her.

Ann's chief objection was going where she could not see Abe Lincoln often, for his surveying was already taking him much away, and they both knew he could not find time often to visit the farm. It was also decided at this time that the wedding of Ann and Abe should be postponed for a year.

"Ann needs more education," Mr. Rutledge had said, "and a woman has to get what she is going to before she has the cares of a home and family. And, too, you should finish your law course. Then you and Ann can set out in life together."

"Perhaps you are right," Abe Lincoln said. "Of course I want Ann, and the sooner the better. But I can't support her yet, and I guess it's not fair to take her away."

"I wasn't thinking of that at all. You could get along some way, but you are both young, and a year will soon pass."

Shortly after this Ann began studying with Miss Arminda Rogers, a cultured and efficient instructor who was to prepare her for a year at the Jacksonville Academy, one of the best in the state. Abe Lincoln was to work by day and study by night to finish his law course.

The young people of New Salem were sorry to see Ann leave, but seven miles was not too much of a walk, and many good times were planned. The most important merry-making on hand was a May party to be held on the green beyond New Salem. Abe Lincoln and Ann had both promised to be present, and all the young people in the country about, even to "Baby" Green, were looking forward to it with pleasure.

It was a merry day. Abe Lincoln romped with the small boys. He climbed saplings and twisted the tender branches so they would grow into canes to be some time carried to Springfield. He swung the girls in grapevine swings. He held one end of the jumping rope while Ann Rutledge jumped one hundred, and her combs flew out and her auburn hair went streaming over her shoulders. Then he picked up the combs and tried to twist her hair for her, and the children laughed at his clumsy effort and Ann's funny coiffure. Later they twined a vine with flowers about her, and made her Queen of May, while everybody, young and old, joined hands in a ring and danced around singing:

> "Kneel to the prettiest,
> Bow to the wittiest,
> Kiss her who you love best."

"Who is the prettiest?" Abe Lincoln shouted.

"Ann Rutledge," the children shouted back. Then they dared him to kiss her, which he did while they clapped their hands.

Then the smallest girl, who was "Baby" Green, was told to pick the prettiest man, and she called in her piping voice "Linkin —Linkin," and then screamed with fear lest Ann Rutledge should kiss him and not she herself, and again the children cheered and laughed.

After the games and the merriment Ann and Abe Lincoln slipped away.

"I want to go to my schoolroom," she said.

"Your schoolroom?" he questioned.

"Yes, down to the creek where the ferns grow. I have no such place at the farm, and I miss it, for the fern dell is a schoolroom where I learn wonderful lessons from the growing things, and from the little brook which goes on its unknown way to find its mother, the ocean."

So they started away across the field toward the creek. They did not notice the cloud above their heads until they felt raindrops on their shoulders.

"Let's run," Ann said, "over under the haystacks. It's only a shower."

But before they got to the haystack they were both wet. When Abe Lincoln expressed some concern about Ann she only laughed and said, "Am I sugar or salt that I cannot stand a little water?"

"But you are so hot now. You ran as fast as I did, Ann."

Together they drew close back under the straw and did not mind the minutes lost, for there was always much to talk about.

When the shower had passed, they went on around the hill down to the creek. Here they found the little stream considerably swollen. Coming to the place where, on the opposite bank, the ferns were growing, Ann stepped to the water's edge and standing on a stone sang:

> "On Jordan's stormy banks I stand
> And cast a wistful eye."

The next moment Abe Lincoln had taken her in his strong arms and put her across to the other bank.

"Look, Abraham," she said, pointing to the lacy, green leaves. "Do you notice that some are longer than others and greener and stronger? Well, in this difference lies a secret."

She sat down on a shelf of rock and began pushing the brown leaves and mould away from something. Her face was bright with interest. But Abe Lincoln was not yet interested in what she was, but in her. "See, here is the dirt in which this little sickly plant grows and its roots go no farther than this," and she measured a finger length. "But the roots of this big, strong plant go too deep for measurement, and so I learn that the blacker the soil, and the deeper the plant goes into the dark and the silence, the higher it reaches toward the blue sky. Isn't it wonderful that even little plants can preach such great sermons?"

"Tongues in the trees, books in the runnin' brooks, sermons in stones and good in everything," Abe Lincoln repeated.

"That sounds like the Bible, but I've never found it there."

"It got left out," he laughed. "Shakespeare put it in his."

Ann smiled, but she had something more to say.

"When I come here, Abraham, I think of you. I can't say you are like a fern, they are too small and weak among the growing things. You are like a wonderful tree that reaches up above every other, and the reason, I am sure, is because the roots of your life have gone deeper into the dark and the silence than the rest of them. When I hear them talking in class meeting about 'growing in grace and the knowledge of God,' I think of you and my ferns, and I say, 'Out of the depths, fresh strength; out of the dark, new life; and even in the gloom we are on the way.'"

He was listening intently now. "But, Ann," he said, "the ferns come to life only to die again."

"Yes, and come back more and better the next season. It is not the special leaf nor flower that is eternal; these are but the forms. It is *life itself* that is eternal. And the burial in the dark does not kill it. Last year there were two leaves here, this year there are six, next year there will be a whole family. It is life more abundant, Abraham, and from it all I learn to go on my way as the brook goes, singing always."

For a moment there was no sound in the fern dell except the tinkling music of the water running over the stones.

"I wonder what it all means," he observed. "Sometimes I feel

that I am a child of some dark tragedy. Again I feel like I am
a child of special Providence. I wonder which I am—perhaps
neither."

"Perhaps both," she said. "Great suffering and great joy
belong to the same soul."

Ann was still sitting on the damp rock with her vine wreath
in her hair. Through the tall trunks of the trees on the bluff
above, the sunlight fell into the ravine, a ray falling across her
head and shoulders.

As if he had forgotten everything else, Abe Lincoln now
turned his attention to her. He looked long and earnestly.

"Ann—Ann—is it true?"

"What?" she said with some surprise.

"That you are mine."

"What a strange question."

"I am afraid sometimes that it is too good to be true. I
have never known such happiness—such riches—such enlarge-
ment of my soul as since I have known you. Many men have
claimed to get to God through his Son. I am findin' my way
through one of his daughters."

"No—no—I am only God's little girl—his little schoolgirl, and
just beginning to learn. Sometimes I cannot understand it from
the preachers, but here God teaches me quite easily."

"God's little girl," he repeated. "Well, I need not be jealous
of Him. He will give me a square deal. He'll not take you away
from me."

"Oh, Abraham," she said, rising hurriedly, "I am going to—
to——," and she sneezed.

"You are catching cold," he said, stooping to pick up the
vine leaves that had fallen from her head. "What did I let you
sit on that damp stone for? I don't know the first thing about
takin' care of a woman."

"You will have plenty of time to learn," she laughed, holding
out her hands for the wreath. "I should like to keep this always,
but it will wither."

"Let us leave the queen's crown on her throne," and he took

the wreath from her and put it on the stone where she had been sitting.

Then, with his strong arms to help her, they left the quiet place, climbed the bluff and hurried home across lots to the Rutledge farm.

CHAPTER XXX

The End of June

It was June. On the farm the young corn shimmered in long green rows. In the corners of fences and along the edges of the woods, wild roses were blooming.

Abe Lincoln and Ann had sent messages back and forth but he had seen her only once since the May party, until the month of June was drawing to a close, when he took time to go out to the farm for an all-night visit.

He found her apparently well and happy, though she was taking cough syrup.

"Ann caught cold at the May party," Mrs. Rutledge said. "It's nothing much, only we don't want her throat to get sore so she cannot sing."

After the early supper Ann and Abraham went out for a walk. "Don't let her stay out too long," Mrs. Rutledge counseled. "Night air and cough syrup don't get on well together."

To them both it was a strangely pleasant walk, for they were both working to the same end; and this night they talked about what the future had in store for them when they should live their lives together.

"By another June we will have our own home," he said. "I

have never had a home. I had a mother with the sort of love without which there can never be a home. But it was not in her power to make our dwellin' place much better than the homes mother animals provide. Our home will never be grand but there will be no other home like it in all the world."

"Then I can help you study, and you can help me. I will have to pry you away from your books, perhaps, and poke food into your mouth."

And so they laughed and planned and kept close to each other until he said, "Ann, you're not going your usual gait tonight. Are you tired?"

"Yes—and I don't know why. I haven't done anything much today. Let's take hold of hands as we did at the May party and play we're children, only I'll walk if you don't mind. How big and strong and comfortable your hand is, Abraham. I could shut my eyes and almost believe it was God leading me on."

He held her hand a little tighter. She stopped a moment to cough.

"Hadn't we better go in, Ann?"

"No. It's such a lovely evening—like the night at the mill, and I do not see you often—not half enough. I could not endure it, only I know that we are both working hard so that just a little later we can be together all the time. Let me stay out a long while with you. I love to be near you."

"As you say," he answered, "but I'm not so forgetful this time," and he took off his coat and wrapped it about her. They went on a little farther until they came to the steps over the stile and here they sat down and he drew her close to him.

Somewhere down in the shadows a whippoorwill called. Then from far across the meadow the drowsy tinkle of a cowbell reached their ears.

"Listen, Ann," Abe said. "It makes me think of the night I heard you singin' on the bluff—the night I fell in love with the soul of you before I knew what your body looked like. The tinkle of a cowbell will make me think of you and your song as long as I live."

"Just as the smell of wild-plum blossoms will make me hear the mellow music of a horn floating over river and trees and make me think of you as long as I live."

"Can't you sing for me, Ann—your pilgrim song? How I would like to hear your clear voice ring out here just now."

"How strong I was then," Ann said reflectively. "It seems a long time ago. Just now I am not so much of a pilgrim as when I herded home the cows. Pilgrims are on the way somewhere, you know, and I'm not traveling much these days—just to my school and back and helping Mother. Will you wait until next time you come? I'll be myself again by then."

"Look—the evenin' star is coming up," he said pointing. "Twilight and evenin' star, and here we two sit together. Isn't it wonderful? The world is new to me, Ann. The same fields are here, the same woods, the same river flowin' between its wooded banks, the same sun, the same people, and yet all is changed —and all because of you. I hold that man to be most pitied of all men who does not know the meanin' of love. I used to wonder just what was meant by the words 'God is love' until I met you. Now I know that *love* is *life*. God is the life of the world. This is love and so with the end of June old things have passed away. All has become new. My cup runneth over."

"Do you know it, Abraham—the rest of it? Let us say it together. 'The Lord is my shepherd; I shall not want. He maketh me to lie down in green pastures; he leadeth me beside the still waters. He restoreth my soul.' . . . We will teach it to our children," said she.

"Our children," he repeated in a strangely changed, new voice. He arose, stepped down the stile and stood looking up at Ann. The pale light fell on her shining hair. Her face was radiant.

"Our children," he again said. "There is one way too sacred for man's understanding. It is the sacred way of woman's crowning glory—Motherhood. I have thought of it—of the mothers of men. The mother of Jesus, what a great mother, yet poor beyond compare. Her baby born in a stable. His life lived close to the hearts of the poor people, His own and His mother's kind. It may be true that the mother would not have been known to the world save through the Son. But without such a mother the world would not have heard of the Son.

"And I think of another mother whose kind face was lit with a holy light of love for her children. She, too, had a son. He was born in a hut. He learned to learn the sufferin' of his mother's kind—the poor. If God shall let him do some little part in makin' the world a better, happier place for the poor and helpless, his mother's name will not be forgotten, for whatever he may do he would not have done without that mother."

While speaking these words the homely man had turned majestic. His long, bent figure seemed in the twilight to rise to a tremendous height. "And in the days to come," he continued, "though I may never reach the shinin' goal of great achievement, the son of Ann Rutledge will, for never yet has any man been blessed with such a mother as she will be."

Ann looked at him in wonderment. For the passing moment she seemed to be near a divinity.

"Abraham," she whispered, "you make me feel like taking off my shoes. This place seems holy and you are its prophet."

They walked slowly toward the house. The shades of night were falling. The far bells sounded at intervals. The evening star looked down on them.

How could the man know as he held the woman that he loved close to him under the violet vale of the calm June night, that it was the little pilgrim's last earthly walk with him?

CHAPTER XXXI

Stronger Than Death

During July, Ann stopped her studies with Miss Rogers until she should get stronger. The weather was hot and she had already made such good preparation for entering the Jacksonville School that her mother thought a little rest would be of benefit to her.

When Abraham Lincoln visited her he found her leaning back in a big chair, a piece of needlework and her little grammar in her lap.

She held out her hand, drew him down to her and kissed him. "I am trying to recall every word my teacher said to me the night I was taught 'To love,'" she said, laughing.

They did not leave the house this time. They talked over much of the past that was happy and made plans for their future and Ann showed him some of the linen towels and table covers she had made and they talked of the books they would have in their little home.

"I should like to hear you read your favorite poem," she said. "Lines of it come to me and make me think—think of many things." So he read the poem, and when it was put aside they went back to their plans and were happy.

After this visit there were several new farms to be surveyed and a town to be platted and Abe did not get back to Ann until near the middle of August. He saw Dr. Allen in New Salem, who told him Ann was not getting along well. "We've never been able to break up the cough, and she's not mending. Better run out, Abe."

Immediately all work was dropped and Abe Lincoln hastened across the country to the Rutledge farm.

He was met by Mrs. Rutledge. She greeted him kindly, but the enthusiasm of her usual motherly greeting was not there. He did not have time to wonder, for he was quietly shown into Ann's room and the door closed.

He found her lying on a bed and in a loose garment not like the trim dresses he had always seen her in. Nor was her fair hair coiled about her head and held with combs, but lay beside the pillow in a long braid. Her cheeks were like wild roses and her violet eyes shone with a strange brightness. She was beautiful, but her face was thin and there was a pinched expression Abe Lincoln did not understand. He looked at her a minute, then bent over and put his arms around her.

"Lift me up, Abraham," she said, "I have wanted you so— have wanted to talk with you, for I have been lying here living over all the happy times we have had, and nobody in all the world would understand but you."

He sat beside her on the bed. She leaned her head against his shoulder, and when he put his arm behind her for a support he could not help but notice how thin she had grown. An expression anxious, inquiring, came over his face. But she was looking up at him.

"We've had such glad, glad days. Do you remember the day the raft stuck? I seem to hear again the mellow tones of the horn floating in over the trees, and I smell plum blossoms."

Abe Lincoln touched his lips to her forehead as she continued. "How little we thought then that God had planned us for each other. Then there was the quilting bee. Do you know, Abraham, I wouldn't have minded your holding my hand under the quilt, if I hadn't felt it was wrong. I liked it. I'm glad now you did it."

Abraham laughed.

"And the evening at the mill when we sat in the dark together. To me that has always seemed a holy time. It was so different from the May party. How we romped and played that day. How the children laughed and sang! How I jumped the rope and—how you kissed me. I didn't count but it must have been a dozen times. And the wreath they put around my head. Wasn't it a pretty wreath? And we skipped away and went 'cross lots to my little schoolroom where you picked me up and carried me across 'Jordan's stormy floods.' "

Again Lincoln laughed. Ann only smiled, but her face was bright with happiness.

"But of them all, Ann—of all the wonderful days or nights the time I heard you singin' on the bluff comes first."

"You have not forgotten that," she said softly.

"Forgotten? I shall never forget—neither in this world nor in the world to come, for that was the night my soul—though I did not know what was the matter with me at the time—began unfoldin' itself from the old life."

"Your soul," she repeated. "Abraham, we believe in souls, don't we?"

"Yes."

"And we believe that—though our bodies through the change called death, drop back into the pond—the new creature in another, better form lives on."

"Yes, Ann—we believe it."

She leaned against him, and breathed heavily for a moment, while he watched her, with puzzled, anxious face.

When she was rested she said: "Did you ever think how swiftly thought travels? We sit here together and our bodies do not move, yet we go to the river and the mill; we go to the woodland and the bluff. I have thought about it and I believe that souls can travel as quickly and as easily as mind—for souls have lain aside the weight of the earthly body, you know. Do you think souls can travel this way?"

"I don't know, Ann."

"I believe it," she said firmly. "Our souls can travel. And so my soul will always go wherever you are. If you are in Vandalia, or Springfield, my soul will be there. If you should get as far away as Chicago, even there my soul will be with you, and though you cannot see my face or hear my voice, you will know.

"Sometime there will come to your heart joy like the wild, glad, singing joy of my life when I could run and shout. It will be then that the singing, shouting soul of Ann Rutledge is quite near, helping you rejoice. Sometimes when you are tired and weak and the way is dark, you will feel new strength bearing you up. It will be the soul of Ann Rutledge, strong and free, trying to help you out of the gloom. And when you feel the force of that strange power that makes you different from all other men—that makes you tenderer and stronger—when you feel something pushing you on to greater things as the wild phlox is pushed through the sod into the sunshine, it knows not how, the soul of Ann Rutledge will be as close as your own breath to whisper her unshaken faith in your effort. Then there will be quiet times, perhaps lonely times, when apart from all the world you will feel a gentle tugging at your heart. It will be the soul of Ann Rutledge saying 'I do not want to be forgotten.' . . . And when you get old, dear, dear Abraham, when your eyes are too dim to see other faces than those of the long-gone past, you will hear her voice who has been sleeping under the grass for fifty years—the voice of Ann Rutledge calling you on—the unforgetting love of Ann Rutledge as strong and fresh as when she shouted on the heights and gave herself to you."

She had been speaking slowly, softly, yet with deep feeling as if half to herself. She was not looking at the man beside her, whose bronzed face had undergone a transformation.

"Ann—Ann," he cried, "for God's sake what are you talkin' about?" And he bent and looked into her face.

"Dear, dear Abraham," she said soothingly, and she held her lips in a close pressure against his forehead, his cheeks, his eyes.

"I did not want to tell you—we are going to part. It seemed I could not. And yet—yet—oh, Abraham!—I am so tired—so tired, and the heart of me beats weaker every day."

He put her back on the pillow and threw himself down beside her. She put her arms about his neck, drew his head against her breast, wiped the tears which were streaming down his brown cheeks and tried to comfort him as a mother comforts a child.

A few moments he sobbed. Then he arose and straightened himself to his full height.

"Ann," he said, "it's all a mistake. I believe there is a God. If there is and He has any heart in Him, He will spare me this. I have had nothin' but you—I ask nothin' but you. I have never loved any woman but you, and I never shall, for none can take your place. If you should be taken away I will never live long enough to get over the loss. God knows this. He is not cruel. He will not let it be so—He will not, Ann!"

He sat down on the edge of the bed and put his arm around her.

"Help me up again," she whispered, and she rested her head on his shoulder. She had been dry-eyed and had spoken with a steady voice. Now there was a sob in her voice and her eyes were blurred with tears as she said: "Put your arms around me —your big, long, strong arms—and hold me tight—tight. Oh, Abraham! if you could only hold me tight enough to keep me here with you! I do not want to be bad, but I do not want to go and leave you—no, not even to be with God! Oh, Abraham! will you pray that I may stay with you—will you?"

"Pray? Pray?" he groaned in pain. "I will pray every minute. I will pray while I walk with my rod and chains, crossin' the fields, skirtin' the woods, walkin' the streets, everywhere I will pray."

Ann coughed and Lincoln put her down. He smoothed the coverlet and brushed back her red-gold hair. Then again he straightened up to his full stature.

"Ann, we've both been frightened. Your cough is better—it is looser. I am sure of it. Isn't it, Ann?"

There was an appeal in his tone and face.

Ann smiled—a bright, sweet smile. To Lincoln it was full of hope. "Nothing hurts me," she answered.

Her smile was reassuring. Something of the anxiety went out of his face. "Yes, you are better. If I were not sure of it I would not leave this house. When I come again you will be still better. God is not going to have it otherwise. I have never done Him any harm."

"Dear, dear Abraham—how I love you. How I shall always love you—here or over there. For though my body is weak, that part of me which loves is strong and well—very strong, and it loves you, my Abraham. It will be yours, and will be with you longer than the mind of man can measure—for I know now that love is stronger than death."

CHAPTER XXXII

The Unfinished Song

During the month of August, 1835, an epidemic, called by different names, one of which was black ague, visited the country about New Salem.

Dr. Allen was busy riding night and day, and Abe Lincoln, who himself had suffered one chill and was taking Peruvian bark to prevent a second one, went with him whenever he could get the time, to nurse the sick and sometimes help make a coffin and bury the dead.

Through Dr. Allen, Abe heard from Ann, the good doctor's information always being that Ann was about the same, and believing her better her big lover went to others who seemed to need him.

Then Davy was stricken down and Abe Lincoln made his plans to go out to the Rutledge farm and stay as long as needed to nurse him. His visit was hastened by news that Ann had had a chill, and he knew, though Dr. Allen's words were few, that he was alarmed. "She must not have another," the good doctor said. "She is too frail to stand it."

With a heart almost stopped by fear Lincoln reached the

farm. His greeting by Mrs. Rutledge and her smiling face reassured him.

"Ann is better, Abe," she said gladly. "She had a terrible chill last night and for a time we were frightened half to death, but she will not have another. She really is better. She is going to mend now. Her fever is dropping off and she does not cough so much. She feels like herself and has been singing. She wants you, Abe," and good Mrs. Rutledge laughed.

As he entered the room Abe Lincoln found Ann propped up in pillows and singing. He almost expected to see her active young form come bounding to meet him. Instead, she held out her hand and with a face wreathed in smiles said: "Dear Abraham, God has answered your prayers, I am going to get well."

"Thank God! Thank God!" he exclaimed fervently. Then he stopped, stood back and looked at her a moment. "Oh, Ann, you look just like an angel!"

"What do you know about angels? Anyway, I'm not going to be an angel. I'm going to stay here to bake your bread and darn your socks and make you eat!"

Dr. Allen had come in shortly after Abe Lincoln and was in the other room standing with Mrs. Rutledge by Davy's bedside. When Mrs. Rutledge heard the happy laughter coming from Abe and Ann she looked at Dr. Allen and said with tears of joy in her eyes, "How good it is to hear Ann laughing again."

Dr. Allen glanced at her questioningly. He said nothing.

Ann was talking again of the beautiful days that were past on which her mind seemed continually to dwell.

"Do you know, Abraham, I cannot tell you how I know it, but I believe I have loved you from the first time I ever saw you, and when you asked me at the mill if you might love me I was almost sorry you did not ask me then if I loved you—only I knew you would not think it right until we sent that letter which was never answered.

"But the night that stands out best of all is the night we covered the coals, for that is when I first felt your good, strong arms about me and your kisses on my lips—and all over my face. And the very best day of all the days was when you put the ring on my finger. Abraham, let's live it over again, that night and that day. I cannot stand with you before the fire now, nor have I been to the table for several weeks. But we can play it, can't we?"

"Yes, indeed—make a Shakespeare play with two scenes. One scene will be by the open fire—one will be the Thanksgivin'."

"And we will be lovers."

"I never intend to be anything else."

"All right, begin. Say it over—just what you did the night by the fire."

Very tenderly and with all the meaning of his soul he said the words her heart was hungry to hear again, and he kissed her.

With a radiant face she reached under the pillow and took out the little gold ring.

"Here's the ring. It won't stay on now. But put it on just as you did, and say the same words. I was so proud and so happy I thought my heart would burst, and my thanksgiving to God was very real."

His face was sober now. He took the ring and the thin white hand, and, repeating the words that had made her so happy, he slipped the ring over her finger as he kissed her again and again. Then he lifted her hand and kissed it.

"You are getting to be a better lover all the time," she said. "Hold out your hand." She put the tips of her fingers in the palm of his hand and the ring dropped from her thin finger. "Keep it for me a little while. Don't let anyone get it and don't lose it. Now shall I sing for you?"

"Yes, Ann—no music this side of heaven will ever be so sweet to me as your singin'."

"Dear old goose." She laughed. "Then hand me my hymn-book."

She turned the pages slowly. "I have sung all the old ones and found some nice new ones. Here is a new song—a happy song:

> "What a mercy is this!
> What a heaven of bliss!
> How unspeakably happy am I,
> Gathered into the fold——"

The song was interrupted by a slight cough which ended in a choking spell. She rested a moment.

"Do you like it, Abraham?"

"Yes, but that's not my song."

"You want the pilgrim song?"

"Yes, my little pilgrim, that is mine. Can you sing it?"

"Yes, indeed, and I want to:

> "I'm a pilgrim and I'm a stranger;
> I can tarry, I can tarry but a night!"

Her voice was clear and steady. There was the same triumphant ring, the same quaver and lengthening of certain syllables. But the strong buoyancy had given place to something suggestive of an echo song, and it seemed to the listening lover that the message came from some more distant heights than the bluff.

"That's the sample," she announced. "If it sounds all right I'll begin again and sing through from the first—sing it all. But Abraham, put the big shawl, that's on the foot of the bed, up here handy."

"Are you cold, Ann?"

"No, not yet—but I feel—feel strange."

He put the shawl beside her.

"It's handy now. I'll sing."

Again she sang the lines "I'm a pilgrim—I'm a stranger——" She was singing slower now. When she came to the words "I can tarry," she stopped a moment. "The shawl, Abraham, wrap it around me tightly."

"Let me call your mother," he said as he wrapped the shawl about her.

"Not just yet—not until I finish my song. I will hurry. I can tarry—I can tarry——"

Again the song was interrupted by a struggle for breath, and she seemed to be swallowing something.

"Put your arms around me—I want to finish." Her voice wavered. She shivered. Then came the words quite clearly, but sounding very far away, "Do—not—detain—me——"

Again there was a slight struggle for breath, and her head fell against his breast.

"Ann! Ann! What's the matter, Ann?"

She did not answer.

He put his hand under her chin and turned her face toward him. A film was forming over the half-closed violet eyes.

"Ann! My God! Ann!" The words were wrung from him now in fear and agony.

Warm and close she lay in his arms like a little child—but she was silent.

He placed her on the pillow and called to her again. He wrapped his fingers about her wrist. He put his ear against her breast, half groaning, half calling, "Ann! Ann!"

It was still in the room. He arose from the bedside and slightly raising his face, which was drawn and ash-gray, he called, "Ann! Ann!"

Again the silence.

Then with such a groan as voices the agony of the human soul, he whispered hoarsely: "My God—why hast Thou forsaken me!"

A moment later, Mrs. Rutledge and Dr. Allen who were standing beside Davy's bedside heard someone step into the doorway.

They looked around. There in the open way that made a rude frame they saw a picture of unutterable sorrow. Deep as the still foundations of the finest soul, the hurt had struck. Like some monarch of a timber line twisted by titanic force, so he seemed to have been ruthlessly stormbeaten out of semblance to his former self. The little lines that had traced their way on a young man's face seemed suddenly to have grown deep as by long erosion, and he was as pallid as a dead child.

He seemed to be making an effort to speak. The muscles of his face twitched. No sound came from his lips, but they framed the word: "Ann!"

"Abraham, what is it?" Mrs. Rutledge cried in alarm.

Dr. Allen ran to Ann's bedside, Mrs. Rutledge following. The man in the doorway waited until he heard a mother crying, "No—no, she is not *dead!*"

Then he was gone.

CHAPTER XXXIII

"Where Is Abe Lincoln?"

News of the death of Ann Rutledge spread quickly, even Snoutful Kelly taking the news to Muddy Point, and though there was much sickness in the vicinity, a large number gathered around the open grave where her young body was to be put away. Even Clary Grove, with a constitutional dislike for funerals, was well represented, and Ole Bar, who had made his boast that he had never been to a "berrying" in his life, stood back behind the trees, holding tight a flower which he had picked to put on the grave.

Most of those present came from a genuine love of Abe and Ann. Some came to see how the strongest man and greatest lover in Sangamon County would take his bitter loss.

These were disappointed. Standing as he did, head and shoulders above any other man in the community, it would have been unnecessary to look for the chief mourner. And yet every eye around the grave searched for Abe Lincoln.

While the preacher was trying to give words of hope and consolation to the bereaved ones it was quiet in the place of graves except for subdued sobs. But when the singers began the old, plaint hymn,

> Asleep in Jesus, blessed sleep,
> From which none ever wakes to weep,

sobs broke out everywhere, for the melody carried to the saddened hearts about the open grave more than the words of the preacher had done, the pain-filled consciousness that the voice of the gladdest, sweetest singer of them all was hushed forever.

After the simple burial rites were over, Nance Cameron, Miss Rogers and others brought armfuls of early goldenrod and asters which they had gathered, to cover the low mound of the best-loved girl in New Salem.

It was not until the company had gone that Ole Bar came out of the woods, and kneeling by the grave, put his lone flower over the place where under the earth her hands were folded.

From the dead, interest turned to the living, and the one question asked by his friends was: "Where is Abe Lincoln?" Dr. Allen asked Mrs. Rutledge. She did not know and asked James Rutledge. He did not know. William Green was asked and Mentor Graham. Nobody knew anything about Lincoln.

Early the morning after the day of the funeral, Katy Kelly looked out and saw a man coming.

"Ma," she called, "there's an old man comin' to our place."

Visitors being almost unheard of out there, Mrs. Kelly looked out. For a moment she seemed puzzled. The man was somewhat stooped and walking slowly. It was none other than Abraham Lincoln.

"Howdy, Mrs. Kelly," he said wearily. "I was passing by and thought I'd stop a minute."

Mrs. Kelly hastened into her one room and cleared off the only chair in the house.

"Ma," whispered Katy, not knowing she had ever seen him before, "what's ailin' of that old man?"

"Shut up," her mother whispered. "His gal's dead, and he's not got over it yet." Then to Lincoln she said: "You look nigh starved, Mr. Linking. We hain't much, but if you was to refuse 'd feel powerful hurt."

"But I'm not hungry at all—I couldn't eat. I've been over about Concord and just stopped to get a drink of water."

"We've got a cow since Kelly got broke up from dram drinkin'. You'll take a cup of milk, I'm sure."

He drank the milk, thanked her and went on. She watched him until he disappeared behind the trees. "He's an awful-sized man to take it to heart so. Don't he know there's as good fish in the sea as has ever been caught?"

The second night that Abe Lincoln was missing a few of his close friends held a council at Dr. Allen's house. William Green was there and Mentor Graham. Dr. Allen had been telling them that Lincoln himself had not been well for several weeks. The suggestion that he might have, in a moment of despair, ended his life was not reasonable to those who knew him. Neither was Dr. Allen of the opinion that the shock would impair his reason.

"Lincoln is large in all ways. He has a great mind and a great heart. He has been a great lover—the greatest lover that ever lived in these parts. Just now he is numbed by the shock of his loss as one is numbed by a great blow. He is somewhere alone in his grief—no telling where. But unless he has food and medical attention, he too may follow Ann shortly. We must find him."

While they were discussing his whereabouts, Lincoln was, as Dr. Allen had supposed, alone with his grief.

After a night by the grave of his dead, Abe Lincoln set out at twilight of the second day to visit the places where she who seemed yet living had lived.

Turning his face toward New Salem he made his way slowly along the well-known roadway to the place where he had dropped his bundle and listened on a never-to-be-forgotten night to a sweet voice singing on the heights. Then he had been a friendly stranger in New Salem. How fast the years had gone! What long and patient waiting and what fulness of joy had been their measure. But now the cup was bitter to the brim with the stupefying potion of dead hope and the gall of human loss.

In the shadow of the bluff he paused. He moved nearer the bluff, raised his face and, with a feverish expectancy, listened

As he stood, the drowsy stillness was broken by the far, faint
tinkle of a cowbell. For a moment the mirage of hope set his
heart beating with spasmodic joy. It was all a fearful dream—
all a heart-crushing unreality. She was yet up on the heights,
alive, glad, singing and shouting. He listened, even straining
his ear for the first notes of her glad, free song.

As if she were not yet beyond sound of his voice he called:
"Ann! Ann!" Again he listened intently.

The gray of twilight deepened. The dim music of the faraway
bell dissolved itself in a pervading hush, and all was still.

In a voice suggesting the pain of a fresh blow, the man in
the shadow whispered with upturned face, "Ann! Ann!" The
whisper, too, was gathered into the all-enveloping gloom and
silence.

He went a little farther on; the soft music of water running
over stones came to his ear. It was the stream in the schoolroom
where ferns had been books and God had been the teacher.

Mechanically he turned toward it. The swollen stream across
which he had carried Ann on a night not so long ago was smaller
now. He stepped across.

The gray of the open road deepened in the fern dell into
gloom. But no light was needed to bring to the vision of the
man the picture of one he yet sought in the land of the living.
Again he saw her with the sunshine falling over the red-gold
tresses of her wreath-bound hair as she sat on the ledge of rock.
Again he heard her voice but he was too numb now to remember
its message.

Groping his way to the stone, he knelt beside it and spread
his hands over the place where she had sat. His fingers came
in contact with dead leaves. Feeling along the way they lay,
he found the wreath, yet there, that had been a crown on May
day. Lifting it gently he cried: "Oh, Ann! Ann! It cannot be.
You have not gone away forever! You will come back to me!
We will have our little home! Oh, Ann! Ann!" His pleading voice
ended in a groan. He dropped his face against the faded leaves.

How long he remained by the rock and the wreath he did

not know. After a time, like a crushed and wounded animal, he crept from the place and proceeded on his way toward the village.

He walked slowly a few minutes, then, as if drawn by some pleasant fancy, he quickened his pace. The roar of the mill dam had caught his ear. He was going to the mill. Here was a place that she had said seemed sacred to her, and he was glad when the dark outlines of the mill stood out against the growing shadows. The double doors stood open, just as they had before. He went into the building and out on the platform over the river, just as he had before. The foam of the falling water shone white in the pale light, just as it had before. The trees cast their shadows and the stars their bright reflections, just as before. He leaned against the doorway as he had done once before when in great gloom, then he waited for the one to come who had brought the light.

Several times he turned toward the door as if expecting to see the fair-faced girl emerging from the dusky gray and coming toward him. In a sort of numb expectancy he waited. Once he reached out his long arm as if to encircle some near object, but there were only shadows in the dark.

After a time he took the little ring from his pocket. He moved near the edge of the platform. He lifted the frail little token of eternal love to his lips and held it there a moment. Then he reached his long arm out over the foaming water and with a groan let the ring fall into the depths of the smoothly flowing Sangamon.

As if loath to leave the place he turned back from the doorway and, leaning against the wall, looked out into the darkness. Shortly after he had done so, someone touched him gently on the arm. With a great start he cried: "Ann! Ann!"

A small figure drew back slightly and a voice said, "I've been lookin' fer you, Abry Linkhorn. You're worse than a bee to run down."

The man hesitated a second, then he held out his hand and said, "Howdy, partner. What did you want with me?"

"I've been numerous in bar hunts as you've heard tell, but I haven't never gone to no berryin', so help me God, but the berryin' of your Ann. And I wouldn't have gone for no one else's 'ceptin' it was you."

"I wish it had been," the man said.

"Maybe so, but since I was thar and you wasn't thar and I heard something that made me pestiferous glad I went, I thought you would like to hear about it."

"You are kind to think of me. What could have made you feel glad?"

"It made me feel glad to learn that God's not—not a damn fool."

"How did you learn this?"

"From the berryin' itself. The parson read out of a book that when this here meat body changes into the other kind like Ann Rutledge has, then death is swallered up in victory. Don't this sound like God's got horse sense?"

"I don't know anything about God." And there was bitterness in the answer.

"Yeh, you do. You know nothin' but God could make a gal like your Ann Rutledge. And if God's not a blame fool he made her for something more than the little time she's spent in this here New Salem. I'm not promiscuous enough to tell it like the parson, but I'm tellin' you, Abry Linkhorn, that when I set by that grave and put my flower over the place where her hands was berried and said what I didn't never have words to say when she was here about, thankin' her for remembering poor Ole Bar, I *know* she heard it. She didn't say nothin', but I seen her smile and I know—I know—curse it, I can't tell what I know. But Ann Rutledge ain't blowed out like no candle. I know this. And I am glad. And I'm glad, too, Abry Linkhorn, that she wasn't none of my gal. If you'd seen James Rutledge standin' beside that grave you'd been glad she wasn't no flesh and blood of yourn. I never knew before that grizzle-tops like him, that's men, and not chipper-perkers, liked gals so well. He didn't make no noise like her mother did, but it's still water that runs deep and he'll have the heart-bleeds for many a changin' moon."

"Poor Rutledge," Lincoln said brokenly. "I must go to see him."

"Yep, and there's others you ought to go to see, and you can't get started none too quick. The whole kit and posse of 'em's about to start searchin' fer you; Clary Grove to boot. Any reason why you should make your friends beat the bushes when walking's good and you ain't no cripple?"

It was this appeal that turned the steps of Lincoln to the home of Dr. Allen as he and William Green yet sat discussing him.

As Ole Bar and Abe Lincoln passed Rutledge Inn, the latter looked across the street. A light burned in the window of the room where Ann's little sewing table had been.

The tall man hesitated and moved on.

CHAPTER XXXIV

For the Things That Are to Be

While Dr. Allen and William Green were yet discussing the strange disappearance of Abe Lincoln, the door opened and he stood before them.

They turned toward him and beheld what seemed a wreckage, wrought by hunger and longing, unrest and the sorrow of a loss which could never be made good. In his face were lines already too deeply cut for Time's erasure.

No word was spoken. The two men seemed awed by the majesty of his silence and strangely moved by his dumb sorrow, and, strong men though they were, tears wet their cheeks.

"Doc," Lincoln said, "how long will this last—for I cannot, cannot bear to think of—of——"

His voice grew unsteady. He did not finish the sentence. Instead he said, "Is there any honorable way I can finish it all?"

"You do not want to finish it. You want to live your life."

"I have lived my life."

The voice seemed far away as if from some ancestral tomb. "I have lived my life. I found it here in New Salem—and I will leave it here."

"No, no. You will feel differently after a while. You will want to live for the things that are to be."

"For the things that are to be? What can a man do when that which alone could make life worth living is taken from it forever?"

"There are other incentives to life than love. There is ambition with its measure of fame, and service with the pleasure of duty," Dr. Allen said.

"Ambition—fame," Lincoln repeated wearily. "What is fame but a bauble—a passin' bauble."

"But think what you may live to do for humanity in some way or another. You have made a good beginning—you have put in the foundation, Lincoln. You might be Governor of Illinois some day. Think then what you might accomplish for liberty—for freedom and justice."

"My interest in these things is dead. Everything is dead."

"No, not dead, only numb. Great pain brings numbness, but Time heals the deepest cuts. The edges stay tender, the old wounds bleed and the scars remain. But in spite of all, the numbness and the pain give way in time to the healing forces of nature."

Lincoln dropped his head wearily on the table. He was ill, tired, hungry, suffering from loss of sleep—all this with the other.

Dr. Allen looked helplessly at Green and wiped his eyes again.

"Abe"—it was Green speaking. "Can't you pull yourself together for a little while—at least until you get Jim Henry's note paid? Tom Dickson from up near Springfield says they're having hard luck. He was over their way and found Jim's wife and baby sick and him about to lose his place. Just a little along now and then will save the day. He was talking about your note, said you would pay every cent of it. On the strength of this they were given more time. This here's a plain duty and a man's job, Abe."

Lincoln raised himself and looked at Green. "Jim Henry's dependin' on me and they've given him more time because my note is good?"

"That's it. And when his wife was down a few months ago

and went to see Ann Rutledge, Ann told her you would pay every cent of it if it was the last act of your life."

"I suppose this is one of the things that are to be," he said, addressing Dr. Allen.

"No doubt. And with the days that follow, new duties and new opportunities will unfold. 'God moves in a mysterious way,' the hymnbook tells us, 'His wonders to perform.' We don't know how or why, but back of it all He moves, and He needs strong men, men not afraid, men who cannot be bought or sold to stand for the interests of the people and the rights of those helpless ones who are always the prey of the powerful and unscrupulous."

"Perhaps you are right," he answered. "I'll not neglect a duty."

Thus it was that the man who did not care to stay in the world to be a governor chose life with all its losses in order to pay an honest debt.

Then William Green delivered a message from "Baby Green" which was a pressing invitation to Abe Lincoln to visit her for the very unselfish reason that the door had mashed her toe and she needed a great, tall horse to ride her.

So Abe Lincoln went home with William Green, where he was fed and looked after by the motherly Aunt Sallie Green and where he was in turn expected to look after "Baby Green." Here children came to romp with him, books and papers were sent, and occasionally several of the old friends from New Salem came out to tell him the political gossip.

Aunt Sallie found something for him to do every night, for she did not want him wandering away to Ann's grave. He made no effort to do so, however, and after a few weeks' rest he returned to New Salem to take up his life as best he could, and day by day live on for the things that were to be.

CHAPTER XXXV

The Poem

The Clary Grove gang were going to have an important meeting. It had been rumored that Windy Batts, who went as a missionary to the Indians, had lost his head. The general satisfaction with which this news had been received by the Clary Grove gang, singly, indicated that it would prove a pleasant topic for discussion, and nobody was likely to disagree with Ole Bar when he said: "Them pizen-shooting injuns has riz to a tall and mighty pre-eminence in my mind if they cut off that fire and brimstone croaker's rattle box."

Kit Parsons was expected to divulge a plan for giving the angels another job. He had been desperately sick during the summer, and while lying at death's door a local religious enemy had said the gates of hell would soon shut Kit in where he had ought to have been before he was born. Kit said he had pulled through to fan the face off this profane wretch with brickbats. The details of the plans expected to prove interesting.

A great horse-swapping horse-story was also expected, provided Buck Thompson reached New Salem that night. He had been up the Ohio River and it was told by a man that passed through Sangamon County that Buck had traded a Yankee out of a horse and got fairly good boot; that he took the horse, fed it some filler, painted its ears, trimmed its tail and dyed it, put a few dapples on its hide and traded it back to the same Yankee for yet more boot.

The group was about the fire when Buck came. He had been away some weeks, and before the storytelling started he wanted to hear something of town affairs.

"Lots of sickness," Kit Parsons said.

"Yeh?" Buck questioned.

"Yes—Grandpa Johnson's dead and Clem Herndon's boy and Ann Rutledge."

Buck was interested now.

"Ann Rutledge dead? No!"

"Yeh—she's dead."

"Abe's gal."

"Dead and buried out near Concord."

"Poor old Abe. Take it hard, did he?"

"Nobody knows. He ain't saying nothin'."

"They say he went crazy for a time," Kit Parsons remarked.

"They lie," said Ole Bar. "Abry Linkhorn hain't never gone nowhere near crazy at no time."

"Maybe he didn't go clear crazy, but Doc Allen said he was hit hard and wasn't likely to git over it no time soon."

"I bet a bottle against a bottle he's over it now," said Buck Thompson. "Who'll take it up? Will you, Jack Armstrong?"

"If it was somebody like you are I would. You get petticoat fever every change of the moon, take it like spring pimples that's always goin' and comin'. But some take it like the smallpox and don't never get over the scars. Abe Lincoln's the kind that will wear the scars."

"Bars is the same," Ole Bar ventured. "Most bars is done with their womenfolks after matin' season. Once in a lifetime you find a pair of bars stickin' together. Nobody but their Maker knows what they do it fur. It's the same with men, and Abry Linkhorn, he picked him out one worth stickin' to.

"Yeh—nobody blames him for gettin' sweet on Ann Rutledge. But poke up the fire and let's get jolly or this dead talk will stir up the spooks."

While they were piling up the fire and stacking up the bottles, someone looked down the road and saw a tall, slightly bent figure approaching in the darkness.

"Boys, he's comin'," Kit Parsons announced.

"Abe Lincoln—or his ghost."

"Thunder—I hope he's not crazy. I kin manage Yankees and niggers—but crazy ones—ugh!" and Thompson shrugged his shoulders.

"Pull in your sorghum-sucker," Ole Bar said shortly, "and don't none of you get nothin' started about his gal."

"That's it," said Jack Armstrong. "If he hain't forgot about her let's help him do it. Let's give him a howlin' good time."

Then they grew silent, for he was approaching and they wondered. They had not seen him since Ann's death.

The fresh flames were throwing fitful lights up into the overhanging brown branches and over the faces of the group, when Lincoln came into the circle of light and, extending his hand here and there, said: "Howdy, boys, howdy."

Something like a sigh of relief passed around the group. He didn't seem crazy.

He dropped himself in the circle of light. Then for the time they saw his face, the effect of which was to bring a respectful silence over the noisy group.

The wind rustled slightly and a couple of brown leaves floated down to the fireside. The gray face looked up a moment. Another leaf was falling. They all watched it.

"Boys," said Lincoln in a voice they did not know, "the leaves are fallin' early."

"Yeh—droppin' early this year."

Again there was a pause. Then he said, "I haven't been with you in a long time."

"Not in a coon's age—and we're glad to have you, Abe."

"I'm glad to be here. I felt as if it would do me good to see you all. And I've brought a poem I want to read if you don't care."

"Is it jolly?"

"Yeh—something damn jolly is what we want."

"No," said Lincoln slowly, "it is not jolly. It's the other kind. But this is my favorite of all poems. May I read it to you?"

"Go to it, Abry Linkhorn," Ole Bar said.

Abe Lincoln took a book from his pocket, opened it and laid it on his knee.

He read as if asking them the question:

"O why should the spirit of mortal be proud?
Like a swift, fleeting meteor, a fast flying cloud;
A flash of the lightning, a break of the wave,
Man passes from life to his rest in the grave."

There was a slight pause. Every man's eye was on the gray face bending over the book in the flickering light.

When he began reading the next verse he lifted his eyes from the pages and looked away, farther away than the circle of brown-branched trees. There was, to the men, a suggestion in his tone of an approach to something strange, perhaps forbidding.

"The leaves of the oak and the willow shall fade,
Be scattered abroad and together be laid."

He paused a moment. Involuntarily several glances were cast toward the leaves lying by the logs at their feet.

He went on:

"And the young and the old, the low and the high,
Shall moulder to dust and together shall lie."

It was very quiet.

"The peasant whose lot is to sow and to reap,
The herdsman who climbs with his goats up the steep,
The beggar who wandered in search of his bread,
Have faded away like the grass that we tread."

There was much more than the words in the reading.

The group about the fire saw the peasant, saw the herdsman. They saw the saint who enjoyed the communion of heaven and the sinner who dared to remain unforgiven. There in the quiet of the night beside the ashes and the flames, he was making all these live—and go their short way.

"So the multitude goes—like the flowers or the weeds

.   .   .   .

So the multitude comes, even these we behold,
To repeat every tale that has ever been told."

Kit Parsons punched the fire. Buck Thompson reached for a bottle and drew his hand back empty.

"We are the same that our fathers have been,

.   .   .   .

We drink the same stream and view the same sun
And run the same course that our fathers have run."

Pausing again, as if a line of thought ran in between the verses, he looked away from the book. The next verse was about the mother and child—each, all are away to their dwelling of rest.

He seemed now hesitating whether or not to proceed. The men watched him without comment. His gray face was marked with a fresh baptism of pain which he seemed to be struggling to put away.

With unsteady voice he read.

"The maid on whose cheek, on whose brow, in whose eye,
Show beauty and pleasure——"

Here there was a long pause. Ole Bar got up and went out. Kit Parsons poked the fire. Buck Thompson took to spitting. But no man spoke as the voice by the fire pronounced the words "her triumphs—are by," and even the fire seemed to burn softly.

For a moment he glanced about the group—a helpless glance of appeal to those strong men. Buck Thompson was drawing his sleeves across his eye, evidently to remove some foreign matter. Jack Armstrong was pinching his red bandanna down under his leg. Another chunk was pitched into the fire.

It was a relief when he went on again to the "Hand of the king that the scepter hath borne," and the "brow of the priest that the miter hath worn." They seemed to see the king and the priest and they felt the force of the words as he read:

"From the death we are shrinking, our fathers would shrink.
To the lives we are clinging, our fathers would cling.
But it speeds from us all—like—a—bird—on—the—wing."

He measured the words off slowly. He was not looking at the book. Perhaps he saw fleet birds winging their way beyond his vision. His listeners divined something of the kind.

He had reached another hard place. He picked up the book and looked at it and replaced it on his knee. Again he was speaking nearer or farther than those just about him.

"They loved—but the story we cannot unfold . . .
They joyed, but the tongue of their gladness is dumb."

"Jo," he said, handing the book to Kelsy, "you know the poem. Finish it for the boys."

Kelsy finished it. But they did not hear him. The poem to them mattered little. The man who had read it meant much.

"What's the name of that there poem?" Buck Thompson asked.

"*Immortality.*"

"Immortality—that means that this here vale of tears is not all that's comin' to us?"

"That's it. We are only here a little while at best. Any good thing therefore that we can do, let's do it. We won't come back this way, you know."

Here Ole Bar returned. They all looked at him inquiringly.

"What you lookin' at?" he growled. "Nothin' the matter with

that poem. But my fool nose she runs like the devil at first frost fall and leaves ain't much good fur shuttin' her off when a poem's goin' on."

His explanation was accepted.

Lincoln was speaking again. "You've been good friends to have, and I want to say, because I won't always be about these parts, that if any of you ever get in need of a friend and Abe Lincoln can help him out, call on him. And I want to say to you that I've lived the best time of my life right here in New Salem—the happiest—and—well, I'll see you again—good-bye, boys." And the tall man, slightly bent and moving as if aged, left the group around the fire.

There was silence about the fire for a full minute.

"Poor Old Abe," said Buck.

"I'd a give my right arm to have kept this here thing from happenin'," said Armstrong.

"Do you fellows recollect," Kit Parsons said, "the man that was through here preaching two years ago—the feller that preached one night about the 'Man of Sorrows'? Recollect how the women bawled? Looked like they couldn't suppress themselves nor get hold of enough dry goods to sop up their flowin' tears. It's just now soakin' into my head the reason of it all."

"Well, what was it?"

"That feller made 'em *see* the man."

Here was thought for reflection.

A moment later Buck Thompson took up a bottle, threw back his head and raised it to his lips, saying as he did so, "I'm glad he didn't say nothin' about Ann Rutledge."

"Ann Rutledge!" exclaimed Ole Bar. "Idiot! Fool! He didn't mention *nothin' else*."

CHAPTER XXXVI

On the Way

It was an October afternoon.

The first frosts had fallen, and where, a few short days before, the goldenrod had shed its autumn glory, it now stood sere and earth-bent. The late asters had lost their color and the windblown tendrils of summer vines were but stiff spirals, clinging to the sumacs like skeletons of their former graceful selves.

In the Concord burial plot all was gray and brown and restful. From the forest of oak and hickory on the one side the leaves had fallen, and lay cradled about the grave and strewn over the grassy slope that led to the little stream where willows held out their slender arms, nude, save for here and there a pale and trembling leaf.

A haze hung over the distant fields which seemed to permeate the near-by woods, giving a tint of filmy softness even to the shadows gathering between the somber tree trunks.

There seemed no living thing about when a man, himself tall and somber as the trees through which he walked, came to the place of graves, and going to one of them fell beside it crying, "Ann! Ann!"

A moment he knelt, speaking the name before he threw

himself full-length with his face upon the sod. Whether he were praying there or weeping or struggling for the grace of resignation, none might know, for no sound came from his lips.

It was not until the sun had dropped behind the treetop that he arose. Yet a little time he tarried. Then he went into the edge of the wood and stood with his sad gray eyes turned to the little mound of earth. As the shadows lengthened, reaching out from the forest toward the grave as if to gather it in, they seemed to bind him in also with the elemental things about him, things rugged, resigned, patient and eternal.

A passing breeze stirred the dead leaves into music like the plaint murmur of some long-forgotten sea, and back in the dusk a lone bird piped, sending onto the stillness a message from the vague and shoreless bounds of some eternal place.

"Out of the depths fresh strength; out of the dark, new light; and even in the gloom we are on the way."

The somber man in the gathering shadows lifted his eyes from the low mound to a cloudbank rimmed with silver. The mask of sorrow seemed suddenly to have softened. A faint smile lit his face as he said reverently, "Soul of Ann Rutledge—yes, I *believe.*"

A bird darted out of the shadows and disappeared in the gray and fading sky.

The man turned and started on his way, like the lone bird, he knew not whither.

Epilogue

The following is the last scene in the dramatized version of *The Soul of Ann Rutledge.*

(*The stage is dark as in scene at the mill. Moonlight outside makes a dim light at one end of the shadowy place. Water falling over the dam gives a soft musical background to the scene. The shadowy form of a tall man walking back and forth is the only life in the picture.*)

LINCOLN (*in voice of pain*): Ann! It's dark. It was always dark until you came! Ann! It can not be! You have not gone away forever! You will come back to me! We will have our little home (*his voice breaks*), our—little home. (*He walks back and forth.*) Was it a dream—a dream of heaven? (*He moves again into the gloom.*)

(*Enter* OLE BAR *left. He softly crosses into the dim light.*)

LINCOLN (*springing toward him*): Ann! Ann!

OLE BAR: 'Tain't Ann, Abry Linkhorn. It's me.

LINCOLN (*disappointed*): You?

OLE BAR: Yep, Abry.

LINCOLN (*in natural voice*): Ole Bar? Howdy, partner, howdy.

OLE BAR: You're worse than a bar to run down. What you doin' here, Abry?

LINCOLN: She found me here once when everything was black. She brought the light. Now I am in the black, the choking black. Somehow I felt—like if I could be here—she might—might not be dead.

OLE BAR: She was alive first time you ever saw her, wasn't she? She is just as 'live now.

LINCOLN (*surprised*): Ann alive?

OLE BAR: Yep.

LINCOLN: I do not understand. Maybe I'm losing my mind.

OLE BAR: You're not losin' nothin', Abry Linkhorn, outside sleep and yer daily fodder. Ye'll be feelin' better when ye get the notion out your bone-bowl that Ann Rutledge is *dead*. Thar ain't no such thing.

LINCOLN (*wearily*): I don't know what you mean.

OLE BAR: Thar ain't no strings on me tellin' I've been numerous in bar hunts, as you've heard tell. But I haven't gone to no berryin', so help me God, but the berryin' of your Ann. I wouldn't have gone fer no one else 'ceptin' it was you.

LINCOLN (*bitterly*): I wish it had been.

OLE BAR: Mebbe so. But it wasn't. Since I was thar and you wasn't thar and I heard somethin' that made me pestiferous glad I went, I thought you'd like to hear about it.

LINCOLN: Kind of you to think of me. I can't imagine what could make you glad at a funeral—at *her*—— (*Stops to steady voice.*)

OLE BAR: It made me feel glad to learn that God's *not a fool*.

LINCOLN (*thoughtfully, after a pause*): God is not a fool. How did you learn this?

OLE BAR: From the berryin' itself. The preacher read from the Book that when this here body changes into the other kind, the kind Ann Rutledge has—then death is swallered up in victory. Don't this sound like God's got hoss sense?

LINCOLN (*bitterly*): I don't know anything about God.

OLE BAR: Yeh, you do. You know nothin' but God could make a gal like Ann Rutledge. And if God's not a blame fool he made her fer somethin' more than the little time she spent in this here New Salem. I'm not promiscuous enough to tell it like the parson, but I'm tellin' you, Abry Linkhorn, that when I set by that grave after the rest was gone and put my flowers over the place where her hands was berried and said what I never had words to say when she was here about thankin' her fer rememberin' poor Ole Bar, I *know* she heard. She didn't say nothin' but I seen her smile and I know. Cuss it, I can't tell what I *do* know. But Ann Rutledge ain't blowed out like no candle. I'm glad she wasn't none of my gal. I never knew before that old grizzle-tops like her pappy loved their gals so deep. He'll have the heartbleeds for many a moon.

LINCOLN: Poor Rutledge! Poor mother! I must go to them.

OLE BAR: Yep. And thar's others you must go to, and you can't git started none too quick. Nobody's seen hide nor hair of you, Abry, since Ann—since she left her tired body and went on. Every idiot's been sayin' to every other idiot, "Whar's Abe?" Now the whole kit and posse of 'em's about to start searchin' fer you, Clary Grove to boot. Any reason why you should make your friends beat the bushes when walkin' is good and you ain't no cripple?

LINCOLN (*sighing deeply*): Cripple? For the walk of life I am crippled forever. I have hoped and hoped. I have worked toward this hope. Now it is dead. There's nothing left to work for.

OLE BAR: Nothin' left to work fer? If you're a man instead of a whinin' rain frog, you'll pull yourself together till you git Jim Henry's note paid. Them Henry's is havin' the devil's own luck. Jim's woman has been down with the black shakes. The hoss fell in the old well and Jim's about to lose the place. On the strength of your note bein' good, they've given him more time.

LINCOLN (*with some interest*): Jim Henry's dependin' on me and they've given him more time because my note is good?

OLE BAR: That's it. When his wife went to see Ann Rutledge, when—before—that is—well, Ann told her you would pay every cent of it if it was the last danged act you ever committed before kickin' off.

LINCOLN (*with more life*): Did Ann say that? Ann would want me to do it. I must do it. I will do it.

OLE BAR: Now ye're sayin' things, Abry.

LINCOLN: I'll do what I say. Tell them. (*He turns away from* OLE BAR, *who, after standing a minute, passes quietly out.*)

LINCOLN: Yes, I'll do as I promised. But— (*His voice grows husky.*) God! If I could only believe that when the dead leaves rustle on her grave and cold rains beat above her breast that she is not there—if only I could believe—I *must* believe— (*He sits down on a box, buries his face in his hands. For a few moments all is quiet save the rhythmical sound of water running over the dam. In the short silence a radiant form takes shape in the deepest shadows. It is* ANN RUTLEDGE, *beautiful in a soft light.*)

ANN'S VOICE: Dear, dear Abraham. I have a new song. Would you like to hear it?

LINCOLN: Ann! Ann! (*He bares his head and holds out his hands.*)

ANN'S VOICE (*singing*):*

There is no death. For me shed not a tear.
The soul's home is not far away—'tis near.
O grieve me not by mourning something lost,
               For I am here.

The soul is more than substance—less than air;
Strong and unfettered I go everywhere.
Forget the grave for I was never there—
               I was never there.

The veil is thin that hides from your dim view,
A form more fair than in earth-life you knew;
And when in hallowed silence you have learned to hear
Love's voice unspoken, you will know that I am near—
               I am near.

(LINCOLN *drops his hat, raises his hands and holds them toward the shining figure. His voice speaks joy as he cries "Ann! Ann!" The drowsy tinkle of a far bell is heard as the curtain drops.*)

*Words and music of this song, titled "Transition," by Bernie Babcock.

Date